SCIENCE AND THE LEADER-FOLLOWER RELATIONSHIP

SHERRI MALOUF, Ph.D. WITH WALLY BOCK

Written by Sherri Malouf, Ph.D. with Wally Bock

Print ISBN: 978-1-7344350-0-9

eBook ISBN: 978-1-7344350-1-6

Front cover image by Shelby Malouf-Pieterse Book design by Matthew D. Hill.

eBook publishing by Hannah Lee.

Printed by ViaTech, in the United States of America. First printing edition 2020.

Publisher: Situation Management Systems, Inc. 339 Nashua Street
Milford NH, 03055 / info@smsinc.com

Includes bibliographical references.

www.situationmanagementsystems.com/SATLFR.php

General/Leadership/Followership/Relationships/ Leader-Follower Relationship

Science/Neuroscience/Systems Science/Social Science/Cybersemiotics/Relationship Science

40008

ACKNOWLEDGEMENTS

There are many folks, who I thank wholeheartedly, for their inspiration and support during my journey. My brother Richard and sister Cynthia with whom I work, stood beside me and believed in me while I spent 5 years doing my PhD. We had to have the long-term vision! Jean-Pierre Isbouts, my Chair, for believing in me from the very beginning. My husband Shawn for putting up with the ribbing that I would leave him when I got my PhD. As I write this, we are still together and today is actually our 25th wedding anniversary. My good friend and colleague Lee Martins, for helping in many ways, including reading this book and giving me feedback. Petra Ingram for her tireless editing and all around support. Matthew Hill for his amazing design and desktop publishing support. My daughter Shelby for her beautiful artwork on the cover. My son Shane for always encouraging me. Charles Cautley, for doing the second rendering of the book after Wally's work, which was another critical step in the evolution of this book. Keidi Keating of Your Book Angel for a last minute final edit and proofing! My entire team at Situation Management Systems, Inc. (SMS, Inc. see Appendix 2 for more information about SMS) for their loyalty, encouragement, and support. And of course, to my amazing parents Toni and LeRoy, for always being wonderful. It takes a village and I truly love my village.

SCIENCE AND THE LEADER-FOLLOWER RELATIONSHIP

SHERRI MALOUF, Ph.D. WITH WALLY BOCK

PREFACE

From a young age, at around 14 or 15 years old, I have been interested in human development, consciousness, and the human condition. Books by Steinbeck, Yogananda, Gandhi, Castaneda, Hesse, Ouspensky, Thoreau, and Kafka had a profound effect on my life. There is a series of books called "The Life and Teachings of the Masters of the Far East" by Baird T. Spaulding that was eye opening!

I attended Plymouth University in the UK and earned a BSc Honours Degree in Economics and Law. I went on to earn an MPhil in Management Research from the University of Bath, also in the UK. This degree was done completely through research and I wrote a thesis called *Management-Shop Floor Contact in a British Factory*. This was my first research project into the relationship between leaders and followers and my Mphil was awarded in 1986.

A friend, who knew of my passion for human development, suggested that I become a trainer for the *Positive Power and Influence®* Program, which is all about human development. That was in 1986, and over thirty years later I am still training with this program. I have taught influence and negotiation programs all over the world, and in industries that range from oil and gas, consumer and pharmaceutical products, to government, manufacturing, engineering, and financial services.

My PhD is in human development and the dissertation is entitled *The Impact of the Implicit Social Elements® on the Quality of the Leader-Follower Relationship*. My biggest challenge with my dissertation was to find a way to write about what can be felt but not seen.

In the *Positive Power and Influence®* Program (see Appendix 1 for a description of the program) we teach people how to use their energy, but for many, this is just a metaphor. However, it is much more than a metaphor, it is science and it drives the quality of relationships. My goal was to find the scientific explanation for the indescribable and abstract complex dynamic called *relationships*, and to conduct both qualitative and quantitative research. The purpose of this book is to explain some of that complexity and science in a way that is easy to read and absorb. After many years of seeing clients suffer from terrible relationships, I decided this is where I needed to focus. I hope, as you read this book, you will find it relevant, useful and meaningful as you seek to build powerful and rewarding relationships in your life.

INTRODUCTION

Jim spun around and stared at the back of his cube. Anyone who saw his clenched jaw and flushed face would know he was angry. But there was no one there to see him. It was after ten PM and Jim was alone on the floor.

He turned back to the computer and read the email again. It was from his boss, MISTER Corbin. "Still not good enough. Fix this before I come in at eight. I will not be embarrassed because some smart-aleck MBA cannot prepare a simple presentation!"

Jim took a deep breath. He'd lost track of the number of times he'd re-worked this slide deck and presentation notes. His boss did not like any of them. He never said what he didn't like or what he wanted to see; it was just "do it again!"

And that, Jim thought, was the last three months in a nutshell. There were hundreds of "gotcha" moments. There were all the comments about "smart-aleck MBAs" and reminders that Mr. Corbin was the boss, and Jim was a rookie. Jim remembered overhearing his boss share one of Jim's ideas, and claim it as his own.

"Well," he thought, "whatever I do won't be good enough, so I might as well tweak this puppy a bit and go home to bed." He made a few changes to the presentation. He decided not to send it right away or Mr. Corbin would think he hadn't worked very hard. So, he set up the email to send in two hours.

"That's it," he thought, "it's time to start looking for a new job. He decided to do that from his computer at home. It would be just like Mr. Corbin to monitor his browser use. The last thing he did before he headed home was flip the bird at Mr. Corbin's empty office.

How can we make sense of this? Some would analyze Mr. Corbin, psychologically diagnosing him with a personality disorder, or behaviorally, advocating that he needs a coach ASAP. Some would suggest that Jim could do a better job of influencing Mr. Corbin, which could make the situation better. In many cases people would analyze this situation focusing on either the leader or the follower.

My research turned the lens away from either the leader or the follower and focused on the relationship between them. Organizations depend on healthy relationships to operate effectively and productively, particularly the relationship between those that lead and those that follow. But how do you forge such relationships?

Understanding this relationship is like working on a puzzle with a constantly shifting picture. Leaders and followers connect in many ways: psychologically, biologically, socially, organizationally, culturally, and environmentally. In other words, there are a lot of different disciplines that can be used to analyze this relationship.

Before we dive into the research, let's consider what a healthy and productive relationship looks like. Let's imagine Jim's situation with a very different boss.

Jim looked at the clock. It was almost eight. He was sure they were getting close. Jim completed the last round of changes, then he texted Art, his boss, to let him know the changes were done. A minute or two later, Art's text came back, "Let's go to video."

Jim looked at their shared screen "What do you think?" he asked Art. "Are we there yet?"

"Just about. Do we have a graphic we can use to illustrate slide 6?"

"No, but I can create one from the numbers."

"Do it. And I think that will put a bow on it. Text me when you are done." Art signed off.

It took Jim an hour to get the graphic just right. Then he showed it to Art.

"Looks good to me," Art said. "Can you think of anything else we can do to make it better?"

"Nope. I think it's good."

"I think so, too. Go home and get some sleep and I'll see you in the morning." Art paused. "If you have one of your brainstorm moments about something else we could do, just make the change. But please be sure to tell me about it."

"Sure thing."

Jim packed up his things and headed for the exit. Before he left, he turned and faced Art's office. He smiled and saluted. Then he went home.

Many elements of a healthy relationship are not explicit. They cannot be verbalized as straightforward intentions or actions. Much of what we experience when we engage with others is unspoken or "implicit." The implicit, while internal, can be read externally and therefore can impact the quality of our relationships. How can we identify and explain these implicit behaviors in ourselves and others? How do they affect our relationships? How can we master the implicit signals that we send and receive to help us create more productive relationships?

I would like to introduce *The Implicit Social Elements*®, which are the key conclusions of my research into the building blocks of healthy leader-follower relationships. *The Implicit Social Elements*® are *trust, fairness, self-control, empathy, status, mutual recognition respect, and reciprocity.* These elements affect every relationship.

Sometimes the application of *The Implicit Social Elements*® will seem like common sense. For example, I am sure you would agree that higher levels of trust would lead to higher quality relationships. However, that is only touching the surface, and we need to dive deeper and ask more difficult questions, such as, "What role does systems thinking play? What is implicit knowledge? How does the brain impact relationships? How do you define close relationships? How can we use *The Implicit Social Elements*® to improve our relationships?"

To answer such questions and unleash the power of *The Implicit Social Elements*®, we will make a foray into science. The next three chapters of this book discuss how systems science, brain science, and relationship science can make or break the leader-follower relationship. These will form the bedrock for *The Implicit Social Elements*®.

In the fourth chapter you will learn about *The Implicit Social Elements*® themselves. Chapter five provides recommendations to leaders and followers on how to use *The Implicit Social Elements*®. In the sixth chapter, through a summary of the book, you will learn how to create thriving relationships using *The Implicit Social Elements*®.

Your journey starts on the next page.

CHAPTER ONE: SYSTEMS SCIENCE

"I really need to quit." That was Jim's first thought the next morning, almost as soon as he opened his eyes. In the beginning, working for Mr. Corbin had been awful, but Jim figured he could win the man over. He worked hard. He learned as much as he could about the company and the industry.

People noticed. One of Mr. Corbin's peers, Sarah, was putting together a high-profile team to find ways of eliminating plastic waste in their manufacturing processes. She wanted Jim to join the team. Jim was excited – this was what he had worked for all those years – first the Masters in Process Engineering and then the MBA. This was his sweet spot! Following company protocol, Sarah asked Mr. Corbin to allow Jim to participate. Both Sarah and Jim expected routine approval.

But Mr. Corbin wasn't pleased at all. He called Jim into his office. Jim stood in front of Mr. Corbin's desk watching him work at his computer. Finally, he turned and raised his head to face Jim. He folded his hands in front of him on the desk.

"I know what you're up to," Mr. Corbin said.

"Sir?"

"You think you can use your position on that team to get more visibility for yourself instead of supporting the work of this department. How disloyal of you! It won't work. And, just to be clear, you're not ready to take on any extra work, either."

Jim was stunned. "But, Mr. Corbin," he began.

"That is all," Mr. Corbin said, "We're done here. You may leave."

Mr. Corbin turned back to his computer. "Go now," he said, without looking up.

Jim needed to think. He went to the cafeteria, got a cup of coffee, and sat down at a table in the back. He wasn't sure how long he sat there until he realized someone was standing across the table from him. He looked up and saw Melanie.

Melanie was Mr. Corbin's executive assistant. Jim met her on one of his first days with the company. At 50 or so, she was older than everyone else on the team. Everyone liked Melanie.

"May I join you?" She eased into a chair across from Jim. "You just had your first torture session in the Corbin cave. So, the first thing I'll tell you is that it's not you. He does it to everyone."

Jim smiled. "What's the second thing?"

"It's like you are marooned on a desert island where there's a monster that likes to torture smart young people, especially if they have an MBA. You have to decide whether you're going to learn how to survive on the island or start building a raft."

"Your advice?"

"Start building a raft. It's not going to get better and you're not going to beat the system."

Jim was silent for a minute. "I don't want him to beat me. I came to this company because of the good things we're doing."

"Suit yourself. In the meantime, I'll put you on my list. I send texts to a select group of good people to let them know when Mr. Corbin is stalking about, looking for someone to torture. When I text 'Shields up!' start looking for a place to hide."

"Shields up?"

"Sorry. I'm a 'trekkie', a Star Trek fan. I wear the costumes, go to the conventions, the whole thing."
Jim remembered that day and smiled. He wasn't ready to quit then, but he reactivated his job search accounts. He figured if he spotted a great opportunity, he'd take it.

Melanie's messages warned him about trouble many times, but Jim still had plenty of visits to the torture chamber. After the one where he got an "unacceptable performance" on his 90-day review, he told Melanie he was going to HR to see about filing a complaint. She advised against it.

"Jim," she said, "you 're a nice, smart, hard-working kid, but you're a novice. Mr. Corbin has been here forever. He knows how to get what he wants and he's best buds with the CEO."

As usual, Melanie was right. There was an investigation by Jeff, an Employee Relations Specialist. Naturally, HR reported the investigation to Mr. Corbin. Naturally, he called Jim in for a torture session beginning with the question, "So, now you're reporting me to HR?" It was an especially uncomfortable torture session, but at least

Jim understood it. It was the way Mr. Corbin treated people. Jim's meeting with Jeff was an entirely different experience.

Jeff seemed like a nice, competent fellow when he interviewed Jim, so Jim expected something positive from the investigation. Now, he didn't know what to expect as he closed Jeff's office door and sat down across from him.

"I know you're disappointed," Jeff began, "and I think we owe you some information." He waited for Jim's permission before he went on. Jim gestured for him to continue.

"You may not believe it, but John Corbin saved this company about forty years ago. He was younger than you are now when he joined this company. We were in bad shape. Our engineering and business systems were antiquated. We weren't bankrupt, but we were very close to it.

The man's a heck of an engineer and he does not know how to give up. He rammed through improvement after improvement until we became a place where engineers wanted to work. When he got here, line workers changed into street clothes before they headed home. It wasn't long until they went home in their company outfit, to show off where they worked."

Jim was stunned. The idea of Mr. Corbin as an innovative company hero didn't fit the man known for his "torture sessions."

Jeff continued.
"For years we had our pick of the best engineers. John

Corbin trained them all, including Barry West."

"The CEO? He's the best. He's one of the reasons I wanted to come here."

"I know," Jeff smiled. "You told me that when we had our first interview. It's why I thought you needed to hear some of the background. Can I go on?"

Jim nodded. Jeff continued.

"Mr. West knows what Corbin's like now. Other companies would probably fire him, but Mr. West says that's not the kind of company we want to be. John Corbin saved the company, so he'll have a place here until he retires in a couple of years."

"OK," Jim said, "That makes sense, but when did Mr. Corbin turn into the torture master?"

"That was probably when the board put a bunch of hot-shot MBAs in charge and they started cutting corners and trimming costs. For about a decade, it was all about making the financials look good at the expense of the products and the customers.

Everything Corbin stood for was high quality. You probably know the part of the story about Barry West putting together a group of the old-time employees and buying the company. What he had no way of knowing is that by the time that was done, Corbin was the bitter soul you see today. His engineering skills had stopped developing, too."

Jim sat back and turned it all over in his mind. Jeff let him process what he'd heard. The silence dragged on. Finally,

Jim leaned forward.

"OK, Jeff, why are you telling me all this?"

"I think you're the kind of person this company needs. You told me you came here because you bought Mr. West's vision of being 'a responsible company that builds great products and great customer relationships.' You've got good skills and you're tough."
 "So," Jim asked, "what do you think I should do?"

"Hang tough and learn everything you can from Corbin."

Jim thought about that for a few weeks following his meeting with Jeff. He wasn't sure he could 'hang tough.' He couldn't imagine anything he could learn from Mr. Corbin.

He kept doing a good job while he tried to figure it out. So today, he got to the office before Mr. Corbin. Jim made sure the AV was ready to go in the conference room and the last version of the presentation was on the network. Everything was set for Mr. Corbin to present his "big idea" for reengineering the company's manufacturing processes to the executive committee at 8:15.

After his meeting with Jeff, Jim realized that Mr. Corbin was trying to recreate his glory days. That made Jim a little sad and it made Mr. Corbin seem a little more human.

Mr. Corbin arrived around eight and went straight to his office. After a few minutes he strode to the elevator and went up to the executive meeting room. Jim sat in his cube and waited.

The first message from Melanie came about fifteen minutes after the meeting had started. "Shields up, people! It's not going very well in here."

About an hour later, she sent another message. "They're wrapping up. Brace yourselves." Jim asked if the slides were a problem. Melanie assured him the slides were fine.

Mr. Corbin strode out of the elevator and down the corridor to his office. The door slammed. Then, another message from Melanie. "All right boys and girls, the Supreme Leader wants all of us in the conference room in fifteen minutes."

Twenty-five minutes later, Mr. Corbin walked into the conference room. He asked for quiet and when everyone was silent, he asked Jim to stand.

"Jim's been here about six months, I think, so you probably all know him. He's a very bright young man with an MBA. Jim seems to think he should have my job." Jim had made some suggestions to Mr. Corbin about his idea for the presentation, but Mr. Corbin rejected all of Jim's ideas.

That was the beginning of a diatribe about how Mr. Corbin's presentation of his great idea had been "sabotaged." Somehow, Jim had screwed up the presentation in Mr. Corbin's eyes, and that was why his idea was rejected. Jim started to say something, but Melanie caught his eye and shook her head. So, he stood silently, praying this would be over soon. Everyone else in the room squirmed and looked down at the floor.

When the meeting was over, Jim sent a text to Melanie. It said, "you're right. I can't beat the system. Time to build a raft." That evening he began searching for a new job in earnest.

Let's dig into the sciences. Systems science will give you an understanding of basic systems thinking. The system science model called *The Evolutionary Model of Knowledge* will help you understand how and why we create systems and how these systems affect the leader-follower relationship.

Systems science can be a complex and abstract topic and the content here requires the reader to have courage and conviction to absorb and assimilate. It will be worth it!

Systems Science Basics

I probably don't need to convince you that systems are important, and that an effective leader or follower must master "systems thinking." This morning, Amazon returned more than 50,000 titles when I searched for books on "systems." There are many similar but slightly different definitions of what systems and systems thinking are. So, let's take a moment to talk about systems.

Here is a familiar system. Your home probably has either a cooling or a heating system. The purpose of the cooling or heating system is to keep your home at a comfortable temperature. The system has a cooling or heating source, a thermostat, and ducts or radiators to cool or heat the rooms in your home. Those parts work together to keep your rooms at a comfortable temperature.

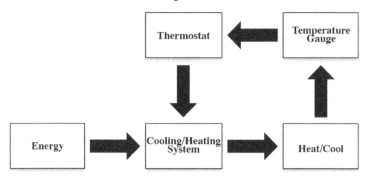

The process of the components working together is what makes a system a system, and not just a collection of different parts. Remove any component – the thermostat, the cooling or heating source, or the ducts/radiators – and the system won't work. This is a mechanical system with a defined function and limited potential to adapt beyond temperature sensing and heating or cooling.

Environmental scientist Donella Meadows says: "a system is a set of things – people, cells, molecules, or whatever – interconnected in such a way that they produce their own set of behaviors over time". Donella is referring here to living systems. Living systems are different from mechanical systems like your home's heating system.

Living systems are self-organized systems that have flows of information, energy, and matter that interact and have relationships with their environment. When those relationships change, living systems can adapt and in this way, living systems are different from mechanical systems. The wolves in Yellowstone National Park provide a great example of a living system.

Wolves were part of the ecosystem in the park until they were driven to extinction almost a century ago. When that happened, the ecosystem changed in ways no one anticipated. Some species of animals and plants began to disappear. By 1995, there was only one beaver colony left in the park.

Grey wolves were reintroduced back into Yellowstone and with it, scientists noticed that the elk population dropped. In turn, this led to an increase in aspen and willow trees, which resulted in a recovery of the beaver and songbird populations. By 2019, there were nine beaver colonies in the park.

"What we're finding is that ecosystems are incredibly complex," says

Doug Smith, the environmental biologist in charge of the Yellowstone Wolf Project.

Ecosystems are what we call "complex, adaptive systems". So are human beings. Our bodies are complex and constantly adapting to the surrounding ecosystem. Then we have the complexity of psychological and social systems, to which our brain is constantly adapting to increase understanding, mastery, survival, and to thrive.

When your home's cooling/heating system breaks down, you can diagnose the problem by looking at the parts. We can predict the performance of the system, too. Complex, adaptive systems however are different. In complex systems, aspects emerge that we cannot understand just by reducing the system to its parts. When the wolves became extinct in Yellowstone, no one expected the beaver population to decline or the aspen trees to disappear.

Part of the attraction of systems thinking is that we can clearly define the issue. When looking at a challenge to be addressed, we draw boundaries around the problems or challenges to define what we need to diagnose.

Consider the treatment of diabetes in different traditions. In many cases, western physicians may only look at the cardiovascular system and make recommendations based on this system only - such as insulin treatment. In Eastern medicine, the diagnosis would not be isolated to the cardiovascular system. Instead, the boundary would encompass holistically the physiological, emotional, and psychological systems - and while the treatment may include insulin, it would be part of a broader intervention. Both agree that treatment is vital; however, the two traditions create different boundaries which lead to alternative conclusions and treatments.

For leaders and followers, systems overlap and interact. They must be able to see the bigger picture of the situation, while at the same time being able to zero in on the details of any problem or relationship.

A business leader must think about, for example, the financial system that includes profit and loss, while thinking about the product system which includes investment, design, and development.

A follower, who still could be a manager, has their own systems - teams that they work with, peers in different functions with different leaders, reporting systems, and so on. The boundaries around their jobs, embedded in systems, varies dramatically.

If we go back to Jim's situation, one can think of Jim at the center of several overlapping systems. He is enmeshed in many social systems: Mr. Corbin, Melanie, and HR. The company culture is a system too that tolerates the behavior of Mr. Corbin. His company also has reporting systems and protocols for many activities. There are also national, cultural, and governmental systems. We could include more systems but then the complexity increases.

The Evolutionary Model of Knowledge

Why do we create systems? How do these systems help us adapt? This section explores why and how we create these systems using *The Evolutionary Model of Knowledge.*

The Evolutionary Model of Knowledge provides a way of looking at why and how systems are created, and how they enable us to understand our individual realities as we move through life. Each person's understanding is unique, and the way our brain creates and understands systems is also unique. As you read over the model, understand that it is called evolutionary because the model empowers us to grow and adapt.

During my research, I read a lot of books and articles about leaders and followers, systems, brain science, etc., and was really fascinated with the work of Søren Brier of the Copenhagen Business School. His work greatly inspired me and provided the structure for The Evolutionary Model of Knowledge, which laid the groundwork for the leader-follower relationship and *The Implicit Social Elements*®. Charles Sanders Peirce paved the way for this model with his concepts of firstness, secondness, and thirdness, which correspond to Levels 1, 2, and 3 which you will read about below. Charles Peirce is the father of pragmatism. He was an amazing philosopher. He stated "for any statement to be meaningful, it must have practical application". That's pragmatism for you!

Brier expanded on Peirce's model and called it the Five-Level Cybersemiotic Framework for the Foundation of Information, Cognition, and Communication. His work was influenced by many systems thinkers, including but not limited to Luhmann, Bateson, Peirce, Lazlo, and many others. "Cybersemiotics" is the discussion of systems as it relates to how meaning is created. For example, why does the word "four" represent the number 4? How did we create language? What do different gestures mean? How do our biological systems play a role in creating meaning? Due to the complexity of this topic, the questions are numerous and wide reaching because it seeks to understand the biological, psychological, and social bases of communication. Brier calls it a "transdisciplinary framework."

If you want to get to the meat of his work, pick up a copy of *Cybersemiotics: Why Information Is Not Enough*. I recommend having a reading buddy as the book is a tough read! Hannah Lee was my student reader, who also needed to read the book for her research. We read the book together and spent hours discussing our interpretation of his arguments.

I extended and built on Brier's cybersemiotic framework to illuminate the dynamics of communication between leaders and followers. This framework, or The Evolutionary Model of Knowledge, helps us to understand why we create systems, how we make sense of our experiences, and how we create meaning from our interactions.

The Evolutionary Model of Knowledge consists of the same five levels as in Brier's work, and these levels occur repeatedly in our lives interacting and impacting one another. Levels 1-4 are all internal and often unconscious, whereas Level 5 is reality-based. The five evolutionary, or developmental, levels are:

Level 1	Pure Potential	Before there is anything, there is potential. This level is constantly in play and influences everything.
Level 2	Pure Experience	Conscious and unconscious experience without judgment.
Level 3	Pure Synthesis	Making sense of experience.
Level 4	Pure Intention	Judgment and conscious/unconscious choice.
Level 5	Pure Lived Reality	Where meaning is created and understood through interactions.

You may be wondering why the word "pure" is used to describe each level. I use "pure" to emphasize that in each case the levels are spotless, free from dirt. More firmly, the levels are free from any manipulation - they just simply exist.

Each level sets up the next one to some degree. Level 1 - *Pure Potential* - is the catalyst and driver of the experience in Level 2 - *Pure Experience*. You make sense of that experience in Level 3 - *Pure Synthesis*. The sense you make drives intention in Level 4 - *Pure Intention*. Your intention determines how you interact at Level 5 - *Pure Lived Reality*.

There are a lot of levels before we reach the point of interacting with each other, but they can be experienced in nanoseconds. As we go through the levels, many times they are so unconscious and automatic that we may fail to understand our impact in relationships.

Level 1: Pure Potential

Pure potential permeates everything that exists, but on a level beyond our senses. When you have an interaction with someone, you always have the potential to create whatever you want to create in that moment.

This is the gas in the engine or the wind in the sails of a boat. It's the source of our energy. We transform it when we use it. We create memories, relationships, cool gadgets with it every day. Creation is non-stop because pure potential is non-stop. According to physics, reality, or the multiverse, is constantly expanding so every moment is one of creation. Every moment has pure potential.

You may be unable to sense pure potential consciously, but there is pure potential in every moment whether you are aware of it or not. Making yourself aware of the potential empowers you to be more open to opportunities and to better shape your interactions. For example, you have the ability to go into conversations knowing, that even with negative relationships, you always have the pure potential to create a productive interaction.

As we think about Jim and Mr. Corbin, at any point in time, either one or both could shift into a more productive relationship, but both were stuck in their anger, fear, and frustration with the other.

In the leader-follower relationship, if both the leader and follower believe that every moment has pure potential to create something new or different, they can be more creative in, for example, solving problems versus trying to assign blame.

Level 2: Pure Experience

Pure experience is the unconscious and conscious experience of events in our lives. Human beings are capable of pure experience - the peacefulness and radiance of a sleeping baby, the joy of a silly puppy, the warmth of a lover's gaze, or the extreme dislike of a bully.

At the level of Pure Experience, there is no interpretation, only conscious and unconscious experience. We experience feelings first in the body before we label them. Emotions are energy. The emotion of anger and the emotion we label love have different energetic vibrations. Neuroscientist Dr. Candace Pert describes how emotions biochemically affect your body. But nothing happens with the emotions at this level as they are just energy.

Looking at how this applies to our narrative, when Mr. Corbin called Jim into his office, Mr. Corbin made Jim stand in front of the desk while Mr. Corbin worked at his computer. Jim observed Mr. Corbin. He experienced the sensations of standing. He experienced the light and temperature in the room. He also experienced confusion, perhaps even resentment or anger, and was stunned.

When a leader and follower feel good about their relationship, they experience satisfaction. This feeling comes from the quality of the relationship. Different interactions may cause different experiences. A negative experience may cause either the leader or the follower to feel that the relationship is "us versus them."

Pure Experience happens in less than a second. It often passes by so quickly that you will not be aware of it. Indeed, we quickly move beyond pure experience to judgment and labeling of our experiences. As soon as this happens, you have moved away from Level 2 of pure experience and your first conscious awareness of the situation may happen in Level 3.

Level 3: Pure Synthesis

Pure Synthesis is the way we make sense of what is happening to us. We interpret and judge Levels 1 and 2. In level 3 we create systems and these systems help us communicate and solve problems. It is where we compare our mental model of what should be happening to our actual experience.

The wiring of our brains evolved biologically in response to our experiences. Through our experiences, we break things down to look at their parts to analyze and solve problems. As we learn and solve problems, we modify or create biological systems in the form of neural paths or networks. These neural networks are then stored and ready to automatically intervene when the same or similar experience is encountered.

Our brain creates these automatic systems because our brain is designed to conserve energy and be efficient. These systems allow us to quickly judge a situation, a person or an action. If we had to sit down and analyze every moment, we would never make it through a day. However, while these cognitive shortcuts help us every day, they can also cause bias in us that is not always helpful. For example, they could cause us to quickly judge the value of a person and trigger an inappropriate response.

This collection of automated systems helps form part of our implicit knowledge, and this knowledge is stabilized in Level 3. Indeed, we develop a suite of biological, psychological, and social systems that help us interpret situations implicitly and decide how to respond to the experiences in our lives.

Jim, using Pure Synthesis, may unconsciously compare his experience in the moment with something from his past. He might recall a visit to the principal's office when he was in grade school. He might compare Mr. Corbin's behavior with the way his parents taught him to treat others, and thus judge him in a negative way. He might compare Mr. Corbin's behavior to his mental model of the way a good boss would act, and sees how Mr. Corbin falls short of his expectations. This all happens quickly, usually unconsciously, and automatically.

In another example, a follower in discussion with a leader realizes that they are unaware of why a particular person is part of the team. When an explanation is given that this person was part of a group that did a lot of the original research for the new product, the follower's psychological system is possibly triggered with self-doubt (why didn't I know this), the follower is triggered to think about the organizational system of the company thereby creating a better understanding of how things work, and the social system is triggered by thinking about how this new person works, will they get along, etc. All of this creates new neural networks.

Level 4: Pure Intention

We use Pure Synthesis to understand what is happening and if it is in line with what we want. Once we understand, we move into Pure Intention, which is the level where we choose what to do. So, Pure Intention is deciding what we want and how we will act.

A friend, Damon Oliva, stated the following; "The Level 4 – Pure Intention, to me, is where things break out; where we leverage consciousness." Another way of putting it is that once we become aware of our own mental models, habits, reflex behaviors and biases, the unconscious becomes conscious. You now have the freedom to 'choose' – a uniquely human attribute and one that makes us quite distinct from other life forms that necessarily operate on instinct/ genetic programming.

Mr. Corbin may spend a lot of time thinking about how others are out to get him. He may love his authority and think a lot about how he does not want to lose it. A lot of these thoughts may be unconscious and running in the background versus explicit thoughts. That may be why he reacts as though he is being undermined or attacked. Mr. Corbin's actions reveal a manager with unconscious negative intent resulting in a damaged relationship with his follower Jim.

Mr. Corbin is an example of how negative energy of one person in a position of power can dominate and contaminate the whole team. Managers have told me how they sometimes protect their group from senior managers who are bullies. The managers create a pocket of productive working relationships. The group achieves more and the group members are not terrorized. The manager's intent is to not only be a buffer, but to be productive as well.

The core dynamic demonstrated here for the leader-follower relationship is very unhealthy, and rather than having a manager 'protect' a group, the senior managers' behavior needs to be addressed. Such interventions are crucial for the leader-follower relationship, and the tools that we provide will help organizations or individuals implement them effectively. Later, you will see Jim and Mr. Corbin's Level 4 shifts as a result of the intervention of other individuals.

You may have your own unproductive situation or relationship and you will want to make conscious choices about your intent and how you will handle the situation. Continuing as-is will only mean the same unconscious habitual dance you have been doing.

Whatever you spend a lot of time thinking about, either consciously or unconsciously, is what you will create in your life through Level 5 interactions.

Level 5: Pure Lived Reality

Finally, Pure Lived Reality – where all the action is! This is where we act on our conscious and unconscious intentions when we interact with others.

We interact with one another productively and unproductively. We interact with our words, body language, tone of voice, and any combination of the three. The way we interact determines what messages are sent and received, which ultimately impacts how effectively we are able to influence one another. Influence lives and dies in the space between us.

Pure Lived Reality is where we go back to Pure Experience in Level 2 and realize that we may need to modify our mental models in Level 3. We determine what systems we need to use the next time around. This is where we create national, organizational, and individual cultures.

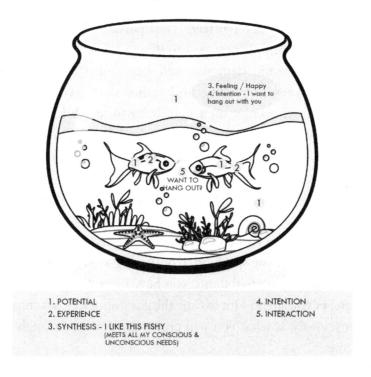

1. POTENTIAL
2. EXPERIENCE
3. SYNTHESIS - I LIKE THIS FISHY
   (MEETS ALL MY CONSCIOUS &
   UNCONSCIOUS NEEDS)

4. INTENTION
5. INTERACTION

I like using a fishbowl as a metaphor as it easily shows that potential permeates everything just as the water in a fishbowl does. You can see how the five levels can occur in a matter of milliseconds and why they can all be unconscious.

All human systems have their genesis in relationships. We influence other people through our relationships. That is how we convince them to support our initiatives in all parts of our lives–personal, work, and community. We base every decision on the quality, or lack thereof, of our relationships. The conscious and unconscious intentions lead to Level 5 interactions. Then, if we are paying attention and are present, we discover if our impact is positive, negative, or neutral.

Think about those people who work for Mr. Corbin. Repeated negative interactions drove them into self-preservation systems and hiding. That type of behavior leads to a downward spiral. They are all exposed to a man who appears suspicious of everyone, and who loves using his power to belittle others.

Surely, followers can rise above the negativity of a moment. But, if the same people face a situation like Jim's, where they cannot get away to reclaim their soul, very few are able to cope. Psychological abuse is a very real and debilitating experience, especially when it is never-ending. Many people experience repeated attacks and negative attention due to attributes beyond their control, e.g. race, gender, or sexual orientation. This is psychological abuse!

Leaders like Mr. Corbin create unhealthy environments, causing people to be absolutely miserable. Fortunately, there are many positive powerful managers and leaders like Sarah, who inspire and build loyalty and admiration.

Jim opened his email to find a lunch invite from Sarah. Obviously, accepting an invitation to have lunch with the VP of Sustainability was a no-brainer.

CHAPTER TWO: BRAIN SCIENCE (NEUROSCIENCE)

As Jim was going through the line, it dawned on him that he had never seen Mr. Corbin in the cafeteria. Mr. Corbin ate in his office, behind a closed door. He always ate alone. Sarah was different. She always ate in the cafeteria and almost always with other people. When he had his food, Jim looked around and spotted Sarah on the other side of the room.

As he walked across the cafeteria, Jim reflected on what he knew about Sarah. She had a PhD in environmental engineering. She was a rising star. And everyone seemed to like her.

When he got to her table, Jim stood quietly, waiting for Sarah to give him permission to sit down. When she noticed him, she just started laughing and waved him to sit. Jim slipped into his seat, wondering what the laughter was about.

"Yup – you're definitely suffering from Corbinitus!" She laughed again. Sarah's laugh was contagious, and Jim couldn't help grinning a little when he asked her, "What? Corbinitus?"

Sarah's shoulders were still shaking a little, and she smiled a big, friendly smile.

"Only people who've got Corbinitus would stand silently and wait for permission to sit. I have seen a lot of it. You're not the first Corbinitus victim, my friend.

"Every engineer in this company gets their start under Mr. Corbin. The powers that be seem to think of it as a rite of passage. I also came in under Mr. Corbin. It's their way of testing people's strength and seeing if they can find the silver lining."

"Silver lining?" Jim asked. He was confused. He thought that the people who run this company were crazy to intentionally submit people to that kind of abuse.

"Yes, the silver lining. Mr. Corbin came into this company as a young engineer and had to fight to get his ideas heard. His ideas were great, even though they were very controversial at the time. He was able to convince the company to take a big risk and the payoff exceeded everyone's expectations, even his!"

Jim still felt a bit perplexed. The manufacturing systems today are old and wasteful, and in urgent need of updating. Sarah noticed his confusion.

"I believe you met with Jeff, and he explained Mr. Corbin to you and suggested that you learn what you can from him. So that's your assignment. Learn what you can from the man."

Jim shrugged a weak OK and resigned himself to further insults and abuse.

Sarah went on to say, "I spoke with Jeff. The two of us are going to meet with Mr. Corbin and convince him to allow you to be on my team."

"OK," Jim thought, *now she's talking!* Hearing those words completely changed Jim's outlook.

"Do you think you can convince him?"

"I think we can. I know that he got turned down in the Executive Committee meeting. That should've softened him a little. And I wouldn't be surprised if Mr. Corbin may be thinking that he was just a little unfair to you. I'll stress what a good engineer you are and not mention the MBA." Sarah was looking thoughtful. She finished her last bite of lunch, and said "OK – nice lunch, let's do it again – learn!" And she was gone.

Jim's head was spinning. He did not know what to think! Obviously, everyone was aware of Mr. Corbin's management style, but they allowed him to continue because of something he did decades ago. And, really, what were the chances that Mr. Corbin would be thinking he'd been unfair? Most importantly, what was he supposed to learn from the man?

Jim turned this over in his mind for several weeks. He was really conflicted about keeping this job and having to deal with Mr. Corbin or looking elsewhere. He was a bit cranky and his girlfriend Lisa asked him what was up. They spent a whole weekend going over the pros and cons but Jim still felt unsure. He also connected with one of his old professors to talk about his situation, and after all of these conversations with friends, Lisa and his old professor, they all gave him the same message: Jim is not a guy who gives up.

Neuroscience Basics

'Neuroscience' seems to be used a lot these days appearing everywhere as an attention-grabbing buzz word. Products are marketed as being "based on neuroscience." Headlines say that they give us the latest scoop, "according to neuroscience." It is worth stepping back and allowing me to give you a little primer on neuroscience.

Neuroscience describes the scientific study of the mechanics of the central nervous system such as its structure, function, genetics and physiology.

Neurons are the basic cells of the brain. They are long and have a central nucleus with "send" and "receive" extensions that connect with other neurons. They connect across a tiny gap called a synapse. Neurons emit an electrical charge and release a chemical, called a neurotransmitter, that either opens or shuts down other neurons where they connect.

If the signal is one that opens, the receiving neuron repeats the same process. Each neuron connects with about 10,000 other neurons. We have about 100 billion neurons that total two million miles in length.

Here's a fun thing to do -- google all the named parts of the brain. One number I found was 169. The frontal lobe alone has 18 different named areas. This is from a list that breaks the brain down into 20 different areas each with its own list of subsections! And yes, every brain is like a snowflake in that no two brains are exactly alike.

We also have neurons outside the brain, but they are connected to it via the spinal cord, and is called the autonomic nervous system. The autonomic nervous system regulates blood pressure, breathing rate, and other bodily processes. It is called "autonomic" because it works autonomously, without conscious control.

Neurons that run along our entire digestive tract are known as "enteric" neurons. The spinal neurons work with the brain. The enteric system operates semi-autonomously and is sometimes called "the second brain." Scanners cannot see enteric neurons, so we cannot study them the way we study other neurons. Interestingly the enteric system has been suggested as the source of our gut feelings and our intuition.

Brain Zones

One aspect of the history of brain science is that people have different thinking quadrants/styles. Ned Herrmann developed brain dominance thinking while working at General Electric. Herrmann was a pioneer in exploring, explicating and expanding the understanding of the brain as a four-quadrant system. He was one of the first to ascertain, through testing, how individuals use or prefer one, two, three or all four possible brain quadrants.

Many would simplify this work and talk about being right or left brained. Yes, there are physical halves to your brain, but since Ned Hermann's time, technology has helped researchers study our brains and develop the understanding that they do their work in networks.

These studies work this way. Researchers put a person into a scanner and ask them to do something such as solving a problem or playing a game. They use scanning technology to "map" the way the neurons fire. Then, scientists analyze the scan results to get an idea of how the brain works under differing conditions, for example in competitive versus cooperative games. This scanning technology has been a boon to brain research allowing scientists to study the brain "in action."

These scans and the research concluded that our brains have many networks with different purposes. They connect across different regions of the brain. They manage everything from my typing on this keyboard to solving a business problem, to exercising and eating. Every action is implemented by a specific set of neurons firing in a specific sequence.

Task Positive Network & Default Mode Network

While I was doing my research, I became fascinated by two of these networks. Neuroscientists first recognized these networks in 1990. They are called the *task positive network and the default mode network*. The task positive network handles activities that are logical and rational in nature. For example when I am solving a problem or creating a budget, my neurons are firing along pathways in the task positive network.

Consider Jim. When he was working on Mr. Corbin's presentation, he was using the task positive network. However, when both Sarah and Jeff asked Jim to learn what he could from Mr. Corbin, Jim was stuck in the task positive network. All he could think about was the fact that the current systems need replacing and that the technology was old. In fact, it appeared to Jim that Mr. Corbin was not current on some of his engineering certifications and he had not kept up with the latest developments. Jim needed to shift to the default mode network.

When I stop typing, or if you look up from the page, something fascinating happens. Brain activity continues, but in a different network. It is the default mode network, and neuroscientist, Dr. Marc Dingman, describes it this way:

"The default mode network is a group of brain regions that show lower levels of activity when we are engaged in a particular task like paying attention but higher levels of activity when we are awake and not involved in any specific mental exercise."

Basically, the task positive network allows us to calculate, analyze, repair, and solve problems. The default mode network handles an array of social tasks and makes social decisions.

We are still learning how these networks of neurons function. Some neuroscientists disagree about whether both networks can operate at the same time. My view is that they can and more research is emerging that supports this claim.

Further research on the default mode network identifies it as one of the largest networks in the brain. In one study, the goal was to map some of the smaller areas of the brain that are accessed by the default mode network and it resulted in this image:

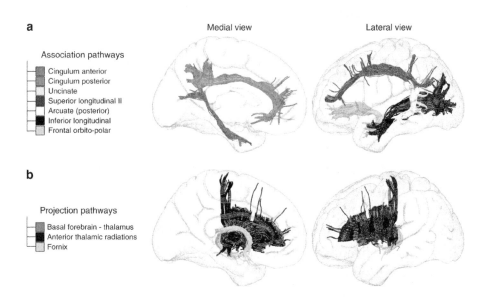

This image is from: Alves, P.N., Foulon, C., Karolis, V. *et al. An improved neuroanatomical model of the default mode network reconciles previous neuroimaging and neuropathological findings.* These diagrams from both the medial and lateral views demonstrate how the default mode network uses more connections between different sections of the brain than previously thought. Structural connections supporting the DMN. a corresponds to the association pathways (meaning within the same hemisphere) connecting the cortical regions of the DMN. b illustrates the projection pathways (connects cortex with lower parts of the brain and spinal cord) mediating the connections between subcortical and cortical regions of the DMN.

The default mode network is critical to our social decisions and involves many different areas of the brain. Social decisions are a vital component of the leader-follower relationship. Three specific abilities are critical to handling relationships successfully. Matthew Lieberman in his book *Social: Why we are wired to connect* labels them as: social connection, understanding what others are thinking and feeling, and social harmony.

Social Connection

From an evolutionary standpoint, as human social networks grew and our brains expanded (attributed to innovation, social learning/ imitation, and social networks: connecting and cooperating with others) we required more developmental time and with it, a stronger dependence on our caregivers. As infants, we needed our caregivers and we instinctively prioritized seeking ways to connect and emotionally pull on them. Being accepted and supported by our community of caregivers was a matter of survival. As we mature this need to connect stays with us, and in turn is triggered as we become caregivers ourselves. Our ability to handle negative emotions is most likely strongly related to our security and self-image within our community and is rooted in our attachment experiences as children.

Therefore, we are biologically wired to need connections with other human beings. Through neuroscience, scans have shown that two-day old infants have an active default mode network to manage the connection with caregivers. Our social coordinator, the default mode network, manages those connections. Further and interestingly, scientists have discovered that in autism the default mode network is inactive. In fact, Lieberman states that if empathy is the pinnacle of the social mind working, then autism is one of its low points.

We feel social and physical pain in the same part of the brain implying that our brains handle social pain and physical pain in the same way. For example, if we accidentally touch a hot stove, the pain is registered in a part of the brain that responds by sending an instruction to our arm to move that hand away quickly from the stove. However, the way we and our brain fix social pain varies dramatically and individually.

The fear of the pain of social rejection combined with our need for love and security is the price we pay for our success as a species. We continue to have this connection need throughout our lives even when we become members of social groups. While it is straightforward to identify this need, the complexity of people and how we handle social pain may make connecting uncomfortable for us. We all vary in our confidence, capabilities, and needs.

When connections are imposed on us, for example through an organizational relationship, it is less natural and often harder to make strong positive connections. The leader-follower relationship is such a scenario of an imposed social connection. When we start a new job, we need to connect with others to understand the rules of this new social group/culture, such as the organization's policies, the leader's preferred mode of working, and the unofficial and unspoken rules within the culture. Beyond seeking success, we are driven to connect with our leaders and peers from a deep part of our being. We have a deep need to be socially accepted and connected in the social groups we join whether imposed or not. Jim did not feel connected to Mr. Corbin, and therefore felt isolated.

Understanding what others are thinking and feeling

Understanding what others are thinking and feeling is called *mentalizing* in research literature. It is founded in the ability to read and understand other people's hopes, fears, goals and intentions. The first step in understanding what someone is doing is through copying. The next and more complex step is to understand why someone does, wants, or says something. This ability allows us to meet the needs of others and build relationships where others feel heard, seen, listened to, and respected. Understanding is a fundamental and essential skill.

A specific set of neurons called mirror neurons fire when an animal performs a specific action and also when the animal observes another animal performing the same action. Observing is key to our copying others actions and therefore these mirror neurons are foundational to helping with our initial understanding of others.

We must understand others to create strong relationships. If we cannot understand why others have the feelings they have, it is very challenging to create solid relationships. As mentioned, the default mode network is key to social decisions and therefore to understanding others. Returning to the example about autism, the autistic mind is challenged to mentalize and therefore struggles to connect socially.

The need for connection between leaders and followers is

important, yet we do not always understand, or perhaps invest the time to understand what each of us actually needs to build such strong relationships. Authentic and empathetic conversations are a necessary part of the development of any relationship but we struggle with how to conduct them. Asking questions of each other about what matters, what is driving us, what each of us needs to be productive are foundational steps to understanding and then connecting. Listening to what people are saying is a huge step in the right direction. Neither Mr. Corbin nor Jim were connecting or listening.

Social Harmony

Social harmonizing enables and empowers us to function in society. Harmonizing differs from connection because while connection concerns the desire to be social, harmonizing is how social values and beliefs influence an individual's own beliefs through neural adaptations. In fact, Lieberman refers to this as the Trojan horse, because these societal beliefs are implanted in us at a very young age as a part of our socialization process.

Self-interest alone creates chaos, so humans have evolved as social beings. Even children modify their behavior to conform to social norms, revealed in my summary of research published in the *Journal of Personality and Social Psychology.*

On the US holiday called Halloween (where children go door-to-door in costumes and collect candy) children approach the door and are met by an adult with a huge bowl of candy. Suddenly the phone rings. The adult instructs the children to take one piece of candy and then leaves the room to answer the phone. Over 50 percent of the children took more than one piece of candy. But when a mirror was put near the bowl so the children could see themselves, less than 10 percent took more than one piece.

Therefore, we need reminding to be a part of the social network and the mirror causes us to move away from self-interest and abide by social norms. We cannot exist in isolation. We thrive as social creatures. We function best as social creatures and the default mode network helps us establish social harmony.

Jim made a shift in his attitude about work and decided to talk to Mr. Corbin.

Jim approached Melanie's desk and said: "Is Mr. Corbin in his office?"

Melanie grinned at him. They both could see Mr. Corbin through the glass wall sitting at his computer. "Um, yup Jim, he's right there." She was amused as she saw Jim grinning.

"Would you please ask him if he has 30 minutes to chat with me?"

"Of course!" Melanie picked up her phone and dialed Mr. Corbin's number.

"Hi Melanie – what's up?" Mr. Corbin said as he looked through the glass wall and spotted Jim.

"Mr. Corbin, Jim would like 30 minutes of your time – can you see him now?"

"Absolutely – send him in."

Jim walked into Mr. Corbin's office. He felt unsure of how to proceed. Sarah and Jeff said he could learn a lot from Mr. Corbin. From what they said, Jim figured he would at least hear some good engineering stories.

Mr. Corbin looked up from his computer and asked, "What can I do for you, Jim?"

Jim suddenly realized that if he thought about Mr. Corbin differently, he actually had a lot of questions.

"Hi Mr. Corbin, I was hoping you could take some time and tell me about what it was like when you started here."

Mr. Corbin initially looked surprised, but then said with a twinkle in his eye, "So, Sarah and Jeff got to you, didn't they?"

Jim flushed red a little – well it felt like he did anyway. "I realize that I have a lot to learn from you." Jim paused for a second before blurting out "tell me stories!"

"So, the hot new MBA is coming to the old man?" Mr. Corbin continued to tease Jim.

"Yes, sir. Bring it on! Tell me what it was like to save the company all those years ago! How did you convince all of those people to go with your ideas?"

"Okay Jim, but there's one condition."

Jim looked up curiously and said "Okay?"
"Call me John, enough of this Mr. Corbin stuff!"

In this dialogue, Jim is using his social intelligence and the default mode network to connect with Mr. Corbin. Curiosity about another person's life and how they think is driven by the default mode network. Jim was so wrapped up in his own victimhood before that he was challenged to see Mr. Corbin – or John – as a thinking, feeling human being. While John Corbin is insensitive and a bully and really needs to shift as well, what is demonstrated above is that Jim shifted from the task positive network to the default mode network in his dealings with John Corbin.

Understanding Our Brain To Better Take Control

Our brains play a critical role in our lives and development. When we are children, we imitate those around us. Our brains adapt by creating structures and networks so that we can be an accepted member of the family/community/country/culture. The child brain is almost 80% the size of an adult brain by the time we are 2 years old, but it continues to mature until we are 25. The brain can continue to evolve and change during our entire lives; whenever we learn something new, we create new neural connections. We know that the healthiest seniors are the ones who continue learning throughout their lives and who are in loving relationships.

I have read and heard many people talk about fear and how the brain is conditioned to continually scan the environment, looking for danger; perhaps that saber-toothed tiger behind the rock. Even though we have evolved enough to drive cars and use cell phones, our brain is still sensitive to these long-gone toothy predators just around the corner.

The amygdala is an ancient part of our brain that responds to environmental and social inputs, and thereby triggers emotional responses. It has been found that children with autism actually have a larger amygdala, which causes increased anxiety and leads to poor social adjustment.

Interestingly, researchers have also focused on the septal area of the brain and found that it plays a role in reducing fear behavior according to Lieberman. The septal area is also critical for maternal caregiving and is connected with the nurse peptide, which releases oxytocin, and the septal region is rich in oxytocin receptors. It seems that the septal area may actually calm and reduce our fear reaction.

We have to consciously choose not to be triggered by people who might be the modern version of saber-toothed tigers. Think about Jim when Mr. Corbin was accusing him of sabotaging Mr. Corbin's presentation so that Jim could get his job. Sure, it was stressful, but Jim stayed in control. He did not attack Mr. Corbin. He did not run away, even though he wanted to.

Our body is an amazing collection of systems that collaborate, so we can survive and thrive. We tend not to think about our bodies, except when we become ill. We take the miracle that occurs every day for granted. However, I believe that we can all do better. My call is for you to wake up, use conscious intention, and use your powers for good and not evil! Or, as was said in Spiderman "With great power comes great responsibility."

So, how does this all translate to the leader-follower relationship? First of all, increase your understanding that we operate within a web of systems as described in Chapter 1 on systems science. Then, become more aware that your brain is actually programmed to run efficiently and in many cases, automatically. This automaticity enables us to get a lot done in a day, but it can also cause damage when we are unconscious about relationships. Finally, take on board the deep-seated need in us to be socially accepted and connected, to abide by social norms, and that the key to building these connections and relationships is in the understanding of others.

Self-awareness is a critical aspect of creating productive relationships. This includes knowing how you react, understanding why you react, and having self-control, all of which enable you to make conscious choices in challenging situations.

The fact that we are for the most part suppressing our selfish desires to be a part of a company, team, group etc., is powerful. What many of us do not understand is why people react strongly to different events where they feel disrespected, or that something feels unfair. It unconsciously pushes buttons in people as it is a part of their programming or socialization as children. Leaders and followers need to understand the dynamics at play in order to have the self-awareness and self-control to make conscious choices and build strong respectful relationships.

We have covered a lot in this chapter about how the brain impacts our outlook, needs, and behaviors. Much is unconscious and implicit, rooted in the physics of the brain, as well as our childhood socialization. Knowledge about the brain allows us to be less of a victim to its implicit and unconscious powers. Understanding empowers us to take more control, use our brain more powerfully, and connect better with people to develop more productive relationships. Indeed, it helps us to build stronger leader-follower relationships.

In the next chapter, we will look at one more piece of the systems puzzle. We will look through the lens of Relationship Science.

CHAPTER THREE: RELATIONSHIP SCIENCE

Jim walked away from the "30-minute meeting" three hours later. He felt humbled about how much John had done, the politics he had fought, the creativity of his solutions using the now-outdated technology. He understood now that John felt left behind and passed over.

Jim never thought he would feel empathy for a man who had treated him so badly. John actually apologized to him!

"Jim," John had said, "I owe you an apology."

Jim was stunned. "What do you want to apologize for?" he asked. John looked sad.

"I misread you. I really thought you were trying to undermine me, but I realize I was being kind of dumb. I should've listened to your suggestions. Maybe that executive meeting wouldn't have gone down the tubes so badly. I'm sorry, Jim, that I've been so hard on you."

Jim was totally taken aback. He felt awkward and he did not know what to say. He realized his mouth was hanging open and he quickly shut it. He could hardly form words as he stammered, "But John …; um …; it's ok … it's …" His voice trailed off.

"No, Jim. It's not okay. I will also apologize publicly. I tore into you publicly and I will apologize publicly. That's only right."

Jim wanted to reply, but the words wouldn't come.

"Please set up a meeting tomorrow with the team, and let's get started on a new proposal working alongside Sarah's team," John said. "Are you sure you can handle being on both teams?"

"Yes sir, Mr. Corbin …; I mean John – that sounds great!"

Relationship Basics

The relationship between Jim and his boss just changed. The boss was not "Mr. Corbin" anymore. Now he was "John." Every human creation exists because of relationships. We would not have language without relationships. We would not have culture without relationships. We would not have organizations without relationships.

As mentioned in Chapter 2, an infant cannot survive without the relationship with its caregivers. This early relationship triggers the creation of models in our brain, and may program many of us for the rest of our lives. Biologically, in the case of a mother, the cry of a baby triggers her maternal instincts by releasing neurotransmitters that cause her to automatically attend to the child. Such brain science conditioning and programming may shape the behavior of the infant and the caregiver, which they carry implicitly and unconsciously through their lives, strongly influencing how they create and maintain connections and relationships.

As the parent-child relationship develops, the parents learn how to care for their child. They learn things by talking to or watching others in their immediate social groups. They learn from reading books or watching videos created by their extended social network. They also learn from just 'doing', learning from mistakes and through other experiences. Parents often do tasks reactively or automatically, becoming more automatic as their learnings increase. Our parent's influence on the programming of our brain is significant, which we may carry over to our adulthood, molding our behaviors and our approach to relationships for many years.

Our relationships are also influenced by how much we trust other people. Psychologist John Bowlby addressed this in his research on Attachment Theory. It states that over the first year of life, an infant will create mental models based on interactions with caregivers, how much their needs have been met, and their self-worth. When it comes to our attachment style, some think that our attachment-needs develop over our lifetime. Some researchers think our initial relationships with caregivers impacts the leader-follower relationship, others believe it is the current relationship quality that determines our attachment style. Whichever way, the leader-follower relationship must also include a look at close relationship theory.

Close relationships are the most special to us. Over time, we use many shared experiences to weave a stronger bond. Close relationships feature interdependence, mutual influence, and trust. They foster responsiveness, respect, support, plans, and shared goals.

When it comes to close relationships, some refer to a destiny mindset versus a growth mindset. A destiny mindset believes in fate and the inevitability of things and waits to see how things turn out. A growth mindset believes that a relationship will grow from experiences and it works out all the differences over time.

Kahle's List of Values (LOV)

Let's look at a study that reinforces the fact that for most people, relationships are critical.

In the early 1980s, Professor Lynn Kahle of the University of Oregon was one of several researchers exploring the importance of values in human behavior. He developed the Kahle List of Values (LOV) to measure how values determine human behavior.

In his original study, Kahle asked 2,264 participants to indicate their most important and second most important values from a list of values. The list included: sense of belonging; fun-enjoyment-excitement; warm relationships with others; self-fulfillment; being well respected; security, self-respect; and sense of accomplishment. Participants then answered a range of questions looking at all aspects of their lives. Their descriptions were cross-referenced with their two most important values creating definitions for the values.

The most frequently chosen first value was 'self-respect'. Those who chose self-respect as their first value most frequently chose 'warm relationships with others' as their second value. The next most frequently chosen pair was first 'security' and second 'warm relationships with others'. In fact, 'warm relationships with others' was chosen as the second value for six out of the other seven values.

Kahle's study is over 30 years old, but recent research has demonstrated that it is still accurate and that relationships are very important. In 2008, Australian researchers using the LOV found 'warm relationships with others' was the top first value. So, as with other cases of scientific research, LOV research confirms that relationships are important.

Returning to Jim and John's relationship, initially none of the LOV primary values (e.g. self-respect; warm relationships; security) were able to come to the forefront and develop. As their relationship evolved and Jim shifted his position allowing John the opportunity to shift too, the LOV values started to appear through the haze and take a prime position.

Two Kinds of Knowledge

Next, we will explore the two ways we interact with other people around implicit and explicit knowledge. We can be very unconscious in our reactions to others relying on implicit models, but before we look at implicit models, let us discuss what we mean by explicit and implicit knowledge.

Explicit knowledge is any knowledge that you can write down so others can understand it. A set of instructions for putting together a model airplane is explicit knowledge. *Implicit knowledge* (some call this "tacit knowledge") is practical knowledge that is difficult to put into words. In fact, this practical knowledge is described as a 'gut feeling', learning by doing, and instinct.

When you bake a cake, as an example, the cake recipe is explicit knowledge. Knowing how much is in a pinch of salt or what the right moment is to remove the cake from the oven is implicit knowledge. Based on experience with personal tastes or a particular oven, the chef may add more salt or vary the baking time. We could say that the difference between a mediocre chef and a brilliant chef is intuition or implicit knowledge.

We use both explicit and implicit knowledge to do most things. If you've ever built a model airplane from a kit, you know that the printed instructions may not be enough. An experienced model builder has developed implicit knowledge of the process. He or she will know just how much glue to use and just how to apply it. He or she will know how hard to push parts together. The experienced model builder learns these things by experience.

The amount we use of the explicit and implicit knowledge varies with each task. Our implicit knowledge grows with age and experience. Many times, the difference between an expert and a non-expert may not be education, but may be the implicit knowledge gained from experience.

If we ask an expert to explain how they did something, they may look blankly, shrug their shoulders, and say: "I don't know! I just did it. I did not think about it." Training professionals call this "unconscious competence."

"Intuition" is also implicit knowledge. Some psychologists call it "unconscious thinking." Many people call it "gut instinct" or a "hunch". Intuition is a specific type of implicit knowledge that instinctively tells us that we should investigate, question, or take action, in order to determine the next steps. Intuition specifically involves pattern recognition based on long-term memory built on our experiences. Experience creates the patterns in our brain which we recognize, which in turn triggers our need to listen, ask questions, or make recommendations. We have all felt those moments when we ignored our gut feeling only to beat ourselves up when our intuition was indeed right to ask questions or seek a different approach.

Considering Jim and John's situation, Melanie's advice to Jim on how to deal with Mr. Corbin was explicit knowledge. Jim intuitively knew that meeting with Sarah would be good, which was implicit knowledge. Jim's new approach with John in the meeting was implicit knowledge as well.

Relationship Studies

Relationships have been studied in social, developmental, and clinical psychology, as well as marital and family therapy, communication within sociology, and social cognition.

Studies of social cognition look at the automaticity of the brain and the biological structures that influence how we act in relationships. Social cognition also looks at how we organize our thinking and information about ourselves and others. This drives how we relate to others, which is often quick and automatic.

For example, we classify people as being a part of "us" or a part of "them." We do this in several dimensions. A blond 34-year-old white woman has four potential "us" or "thems" just from her quick description. There is her age, her hair color, her race, and finally her gender. Our brain quickly assesses this categorization. According to Robert Sapolsky, oxytocin is released in the brain for anyone who is considered an "us" or a "them." If the person is an "us", it prompts trust, generosity, and cooperation. When it comes to "them," we become more aggressive and dismissive.

The "us versus them" mindset can be intimidating. What happens if the leader is male and the follower is female? What happens if the leader is white and the follower is a person of color? What happens if the leader is male and the follower is gender diverse? In all of these scenarios, the follower may feel reluctant to speak out if they feel that their difference is making it difficult to connect with their leader. It takes courage to make the first move, but maybe that's all that is needed. In these days of extreme sensitivity, some leaders may be fearful to reach out as it may be misconstrued. Again a leader can set a tone of openness and a follower can respond if they feel that they are being treated unfairly due to their difference. This intervention is best done when both are trusting, therefore building trust may be a good place to begin.

Let us think about Mr. Corbin's reaction to Jim. It is likely that he immediately classified Jim as "them" because he had an MBA. Regardless of evidence, Mr. Corbin treated Jim as if he was one of the MBAs who almost wrecked the company.

But what happened to get Mr. Corbin to make such a dramatic shift? Sarah and Jeff set up a meeting with him to talk about Jim. Here's what happened in that conversation which helped to shift the dynamics of the relationship between Jim and Mr. Corbin.

> Sarah opened the meeting. "Hi John – thanks for meeting with Jeff and me to talk about Jim."
>
> "Two against one?" He really liked Sarah. She was a first-rate engineer and John really respected that. It didn't stop him from giving her a hard time, though.
>
> "Now John," Jeff started to insert, but John interrupted him and said, "Relax Jeff, I'm just kidding around."
>
> "Sometimes it is hard to know with you, John, and I think you like that." Jeff smiled. He was going to say something more when John turned to Sarah.
>
> "Okay now that we're done with the small talk, let's get down to business. What do you want from me, Sarah?"
>
> "Jim." Sarah said the one word and just looked at John calmly.
>
> "Take him. I don't need someone who doesn't help me in my group. He's all yours!" John added dismissively with a wave of his hand. "Are we done?"

Sarah returned his gaze and paused. "Not quite! Do you even realize how amazingly intelligent and creative Jim is? He told me about the suggestions that you turned down. If you had been open to them, you might have gotten approval from the executive committee."

Sarah looked at John for a moment and then continued, "Listen, I know you've had a long and hard road here, but Jim is actually a lot like you were when you first started here."

John shifted uncomfortably in his chair and looked down. Then he started to laugh. "You may be right. He is a big pain in the butt!"

Suddenly there was a knock at the door and Melanie stuck her head in. "Mr. Corbin, Barry would like to join your meeting." Sarah, Jeff, and John all stood up and John said, "Of course, come in Barry," as he gave Sarah a sideways glance. So, this is a real ambush, he thought to himself.

Barry, the CEO, was actually a really nice guy. Everyone liked him, and he was also a respected engineer and businessman. He strode into the room with his beaming smile and shook hands vigorously with John. "Hi, John! Hope you're doing okay. Regarding the executive meeting, we really couldn't see that what you were proposing would work. I am sorry about that. You seem to have taken it really hard."

John felt taken aback by this second reference to a day that he just wanted to forget. "No worries Barry, we have to do what is right for the company," John said, even though he felt like he wasn't being entirely honest.

They all sat down around the conference table in John's office. Barry looked at John and said very simply, "I'm sorry, John! I'm sorry that it didn't go as you wanted it to. I know we haven't always been as good as you've wanted us to be, especially when we were cutting costs left and right. You've always hung in there and I want you to see a new role for yourself."

"What role is that?" John looked perplexed. He had no idea where this was going.

"I want you to take Jim under your wing. I want you to see him as a younger version of yourself. He's brilliant just as you were in the day, but he is a diamond in the rough. You could really help him and bring out his talents. What do you say?"

"Well Barry, do I have a choice?" John looked at Jeff, feeling like it would be a good time for HR to step in and support him.

Jeff looked sympathetically at John and said, "We've always had the new green engineers come in under you. In the beginning you were really good with them, but you seem to have become a little hard on people. I think that you've been hardest on Jim." John bristled a little bit, but Jeff continued, "We all respect you tremendously, John. The work you did for many years was truly groundbreaking. You know innovation. You know creativity. You are a brilliant engineer and you can really make a big difference."

John started reflecting on what they were saying. He has been bored and had all but given up. After the executive committee meeting, he was pretty demotivated. "So, what specifically do you want from me?"

Sarah jumped in and said, "Let's both run teams, mine focusing on sustainability and yours focusing on upgrades and efficiency. Let's have Jim on both teams so that we are not working at cross purposes. What do you think?"

John started thinking about Jim and realized they were right. He was a lot like him. He also realized that he had been really hard on him and he felt a little bit guilty. He was silent for a moment, then he turned to Sarah.

"I like the idea. If we coordinate our efforts, we can bring him along really fast. How about if you and I meet tomorrow and craft a development plan for Jim? Jeff can bring his HR magic. Better yet, let's make it later in the week. I want to apologize to the young man before he discovers how we're going to overwork him."

Relationships and Mental Models

This last conversation helped John shift Jim from a "them" to an "us," and his entire demeanor changed. He sees Jim much differently now. Not only is he an "us," but he is seeing the possibility that Jim may just be able to be a really good follower. His mental model about Jim shifted enabling him to have a much more productive conversation with him.

For relationships, we create what are formally called "schemas" or "mental models." Mental models organize information about ourselves and other people. These mental models can be about people in general and about specific individuals. For example, followers expect leaders to be dedicated, dynamic, and sensitive. Leaders expect followers to be hardworking, productive, and loyal.

We have thoughts and feelings about ourselves, the other person, and how the conversation should go that guide how we react, even if the reaction is unwarranted. We can have multiple models about one person that we use in different situations. Some mental models contain a script.

Think about your close relationships. Do you have the same disagreement with a significant other over and over? In close relationships we may repeatedly have the same disagreement with each other. Interactions in established relationships are often unintentional, uncontrolled, and not consciously implemented. Our automatic reactions can make it hard for us to realize that someone else has changed. We cannot see the other person through a new lens as our mental models have been repeatedly experienced and have become embedded in our brains to the point where we are not open to seeing the other person in a new light.

Remember when Mr. Corbin called Jim into his office for the "torture session?" While Jim stood in front of Mr. Corbin's desk, he was probably comparing Mr. Corbin to Jim's mental model of an ideal leader. This would have been at Level 3, synthesis, so it was probably a mix of conscious and unconscious processing.

These unconscious mental models are created through our experiences and socialization at Level 3 in the Evolutionary Model of Knowledge. While useful, they can be unproductive to our relationships. The brain is conservative. It does not want to create a new model for each interaction, so in the interest of efficiency and energy conservation, it chooses automatic paths that work most of the time. Paying attention is hard work and it takes time and valuable energy, which the body needs for other functions.

Understanding and Using Relationship Science

From this quick discussion of relationships, what have we discovered? We understand that relationships matter a lot to most people. We have implicit mental models that unconsciously cause us to react to other people. Those mental models begin to be formed when we are children and can be based on how we were raised, and they continue to develop through experiences. We know that our brain creates biological structures that help us handle our relationships. We have unconscious expectations for different relationships in our lives. All of these factors mix together into a platform, on which we set relationship expectations, we master our connections, we build our relationships. This drives how we behave with other people in different situations.

In the leader-follower relationship, leaders and followers both have set models and have expectations about the other that may be, for the most part, unconscious. It is not uncommon to hear statements such as 'I know a good leader/follower when I see one.'

Both sides of the leader-follower relationship bring much with them from the conditioning of the brain founded in their relationships as an infant and further formed from their life experiences. Common to both sides is the need for self-respect and warm relationships.

As in any relationship, leaders and followers can make the effort to understand the other person as a foundational step to building a stronger connection. Just from reading this book, we can see that building a productive relationship is complex and much of it is implicit. Understanding the basics of relationship science, system science, and brain science are foundational pieces of the human system puzzle. Understanding will help us to better analyze and thus improve the leader and follower relationship.

As a behavioral scientist and researcher, I used these sciences in my research and created a new structure to enable people to become clear and intentional about building relationships. My final focus on a leader-follower relationship was a journey, which is described in the next chapter - the *7 Implicit Social Elements*® and the role they play in our relationships.

CHAPTER FOUR: IMPLICIT SOCIAL ELEMENTS®

I recognized my deep passion for understanding and helping people to heal relationships. I have spent over thirty years owning and instructing the *Positive Power and Influence* ® (PPI) Program that was developed by two recognized experts in human behavior, David Berlew and Roger Harrison. With PPI, my mission has been to help people build stronger, lasting relationships while achieving their goals. Through this mission I have seen firsthand that PPI has an amazing impact on people, while at the same time I could see that more could be done to help improve relationships.

One thing that I thought about concerning my research was situations where people were under great stress, yet they remained calm and made critical decisions that resolved the situation. They managed to influence the people around them to take action and fix the problem. Imagining people's feelings of fear, frustration, and confusion, this one person, who could be either a leader or a follower, pulled everyone through.

After thinking about these situations and after teaching many people, it became apparent to me that the leader-follower relationship needed addressing. Surprisingly, there is little research focusing on it. However, I was seeing an amazing amount of lost energy and lost results owing to broken leader-follower relationships that were causing stress, frustration and distraction. In fact, seeing the emotions, I became passionate about wanting to make a difference here. So, my PhD morphed from looking at influence into focusing on the leader-follower relationship.

One of the amazing outcomes of doing research and writing my dissertation is that I think differently now. My theoretical argument in my dissertation has a great deal of complexity in it because there is a great deal of complexity in the leader-follower relationships. I did not take the simple path.

I spent a lot of time gazing out of the window and thinking. Part of my process was reading and thinking about all of the literature on leadership that dates back many years. In my thirty years of experience as an adult educator, and as I looked at my industry, I realized that we would never find a leadership training program that would work on its own.

The relationship between leaders and followers, I realized, is key to making all of these leadership models work. Many followers feel ignored, hurt, disappointed, and taken for granted. Many leaders feel like they have tried every leadership program out there and they still feel frustrated when leading people. I realized that they really lacked that connection, that social relationship so critical to the success of organizations.

Journey to *The Implicit Social Elements*®

The core of all leadership behaviors is influencing followers to achieve a common goal by triggering their *social decision-making processes*. This cannot be done without creating a powerful bond and connection through a mutually held and honored social relationship.

Social decision-making involves emotion and the prefrontal cortex, according to a study by Foxall. Bechara found that addicts demonstrate impulse control deficits, are unable to delay gratification, and lack control through the default mode network. This is caused by the interaction between wanting to follow impulses and reflecting on the best choice, both of which are rooted in the default mode network. Leaders seek to trigger followers' self-control through reflection and guide them to support the strategic direction of the organization, as mentioned above - social decision-making.

Rilling and Sanfey created a neural systems model that is activated for nine different types of social decisions. The nine are: deciding to trust another, reciprocate trust, deal with a breach of trust, share resources, deal with inequity, be altruistic, abide by social norms, learn from others, and be competitive in social interactions.

Therefore, I created what I have termed *The Implicit Social Elements®* by combining Rilling and Sanfey's social decision-making model with the work of Boyatzis et al. (2014), Boyatzis, Goleman, & McKee (2013), Lieberman's (2013) three social abilities, implicit leader and follower theories, Kahle's LOV, cybersemiotics, and close relationship theory. This led me to the following elements - trust, fairness, empathy, reciprocity, status, self-control, and mutual recognition respect.

While *The Implicit Social Elements®* are founded on science and my research, as it turns out, they also contain a lot of common sense. Most of us would appreciate a relationship with high levels of trust, fairness, empathy, reciprocity, status, self-control, and mutual recognition respect. Sounds like heaven!

So, what are the *Implicit Social Elements®* They form an unconscious system that uses our implicit knowledge to automatically assess situations and drive how we respond to those situations. I call them "elements" because they are the foundation of all relationships. Some are more important than others to different people, so no two people will have the same exact needs.

The seven *Implicit Social Elements®* can be summarized as follows:

Trust	confidence in the honesty or integrity of a person
Fairness	impartial and just treatment of others
Self-Control	control thoughts, regulate emotions, and inhibit impulses
Empathy	awareness, understanding, and the sharing of another's feelings
Reciprocity	mutual benefit in which both parties gain value
Status	acknowledgement of position and prestige
Mutual Recognition Respect	respect of individual rights and humanity through recognition of everyone's worth and dignity

Trust: Confidence in the Honesty or Integrity of a Person

Common sense tells us that when there is more trust, there is a stronger relationship. There are many studies and training programs on trust. For example, trust has to do with predictability and dependability according to Holmes. In fact, oxytocin is released when a signal of trust is received. Zak, Kurzban, & Matzner found that this leads to more cooperation.

According to the Rilling and Sanfey neural systems model, trust plays a core role in social decisions. Three of the types of social decisions deal with trust and fully utilize implicit knowledge. Most decisions to trust an unknown person are based on several core factors. Reputation plays a role, but so does facial trustworthiness. People judge others almost instantly based on how they look. An untrustworthy face triggers the amygdala and causes fear of betrayal again according to Rilling and Sanfey. They also found that people who can handle a breach of trust without terminating the relationship are likely to be successful.

Trust is mentioned in many places in the literature and another example is that both connection and harmonizing per Lieberman's abilities require trust-building. In the work of Boyatzis, both social and emotional intelligence require trust, and he states that this characterizes exceptional leaders.

Research also supports trust being built through acts of reciprocity. Being trusted and feeling that requests are fulfilled without threats to gain compliance activates the reward region of the brain. In Kahle's LOV (List of Values) model, trust is supported by the values of warm relationships with others and security. In the implicit mental models, it comes under dedication and being reliable.

Literature and common sense tell us that trust is a necessary component of healthy relationships, as it is between a leader and follower. With such relationships imposed, it takes more effort to understand, seek common ground, and build trust. If trust is broken or lacking between the leader-followers, it can be extremely detrimental to the organization's dynamics, creating a drain on the individuals who are forced to work together.

Building trust is a driving motivation for both leaders and followers, and those around the leader feel safer and more confident. Trusting someone means that we give them the benefit of the doubt when there has been a breach of confidence or failure. Leaders cannot always share all of the information with followers, so trust is necessary, otherwise, the followers' distrust will be easily triggered when leaders avoid certain topics.

As our story of Jim and John evolved, we could see that neither trusted the other at the beginning. Jim did not trust John because he felt like he was under constant attack. John did not trust Jim, because he thought that Jim was just another hotshot MBA who wanted his job. They fell into a pattern of mistrust.

Sarah and Jeff worked on Jim and brought in Barry to help with John. Eventually, John and Jim shifted their mindsets about the other and took steps to build trust. Both of them experienced confusion, which is part of a normal change process when we shift out of old ways of thinking.

Fairness: Impartial and Just Treatment of Others

Fairness is a loaded word. Some people think fairness means everyone receives the same reward. Others think fairness should be based on contribution. Still others think it should be based on need. It also includes organizational justice; fairness in how projects are assigned, information is shared, salaries are determined, and people are treated.

Neuroscience research indicates that as long as people feel the process is fair, they are happy with the result. Issues in terms of the absence of fairness turn on the reward machinery in the brain as found by both Lieberman and Rilling & Sanfey.

In Kahle's LOV, fairness is matched with the value of being well respected. Fairness is more important for the follower than the leader, and may be linked with the implicit leader attribute of sensitivity. Fairness is critical in building the leader-follower relationship. Maintaining fairness is one of the connectedness factors that foster equilibrium and resilience.

Different ways of conceiving fairness can result in some strange statements. For example, Jim thought John was fair when he treated everyone the same way, even when he described sessions with John as "torture sessions!" At the same time, he thought it wasn't fair that the organization tolerated John's abusive behavior.

Self-Control: Control Thoughts, Regulate Emotions, and Inhibit Impulses

Self-control does not just regulate emotions; it also enables both leaders and followers to process strong emotions productively. Emotional intelligence is achieved through Lieberman's abilities of connection and harmonizing. A person can think about and actively manage self and emotions to achieve a calm and powerful presence. That, in turn, helps create many of the outcomes we associate with success.

Lieberman states, "People with higher levels of self-control have higher incomes, higher credit scores, better health, and better social skills from childhood to adulthood, and they report being happier with life." All types of self-control (motor, emotional, or cognitive self-control) utilize the same brain functions, but we can only perform one kind of self-control at a time.

Self-control is an antecedent to close personal relationships. It is also about choosing to do unpleasant tasks, doing the right thing, impulse control, staying on schedule, and completing tasks.

In Kahle's LOV, self-control is defined as including self-respect, sense of accomplishment, and self-fulfillment. In the composite results for questions that directly measured self-esteem, the respondents who measured high for self-esteem had either, (a) self-fulfillment, (b) sense of accomplishment, or (c) self-respect as their number one value.

For the implicit leader and follower theories, self-control could be linked with sensitivity for the leader attributes and most of the follower attributes. Self-control could be a very strong element for leaders to see in followers and vice versa. Either one could have a positive impact on the development of the relationship if they demonstrate high levels of self-control.

Jim demonstrates a high level of self-control by not overreacting to John. John's level of self-control is low as he lectures and verbally abuses the people who work for him.

Empathy: Awareness, Understanding, and the Sharing of Another's Feelings

Empathy "is arguably the pinnacle of our social cognitive achievements— the peak of the social brain" according to Lieberman. To empathize with others, we need all the social neural systems we have discussed. Empathy requires coordination of the mentalizing/mirror system and the reward system so we can be present.

We must listen to what others are saying and feel what they are feeling, and then be moved to help them. The idea of being able to "walk in someone else's shoes" means the ability to let go of our own needs, beliefs, and judgments, and be open to someone else's perception of reality. Empathy triggers altruistic behavior and choices. Our brain is designed to stay in our own shoes, we have so much that is unique to each of us, therefore, it is hard to do.

In Kahle's LOV, empathy is reflected by the value of warm relationships with others, which repeatedly came up as a strong value in the surveys. In the implicit theories, the attributes of sensitivity, being a team player, and being loyal are all supported by empathy. Empathy helps us understand others' motives, agendas, and needs, and keeps us connected and informed. It builds trust and fosters our support for others.

Many want leaders to be more empathetic towards followers but it is not a one-way street. When followers understand that a leader also has leaders and that they have to fulfill their role as designated by the company, their relationship with their leader is strengthened.

In the beginning of the relationship between Jim and John, neither had empathy for the other. Neither was thinking about how the other person was feeling or about what they were thinking. Once they started to feel empathy, it was possible to repair the relationship.

Reciprocity: Mutual Benefit in Which Both Parties Gain Value

Reciprocity is the exchange of favors, acts of kindness, gifts, and more. Reciprocity has two drives; while exchange is one, the other one is the social repercussions of not reciprocating.

So, let's say someone does you a favor. When you return the favor, you probably want the other person to know it. We call that the drive for social recognition. But people return favors even when the other person is not aware of it. That is because we have an internalized social norm, the second drive, that returning a favor is the right thing to do according to Burger, Sanchez, Imberi, & Grande. They state that there is a widespread recognition of reciprocity as a norm.

Reciprocity is one of the strongest social norms according to a range of researchers: Cialdini, Lieberman, and Whatley, Webster, Smith, & Rhodes. It is a central feature of human nature that creates social stability. People will reciprocate even when they do not like the donor according to Whatley, et al.

Salazar found that balanced reciprocity is a natural part of healthy relationships of all kinds. But, if one party to the relationship does all the giving, the other party may feel unwanted obligation. Negative reciprocity cycles are also correlated with marital dissatisfaction.

You have probably experienced that our natural drive to reciprocate can cause problems at work. Every workplace has someone who gives favors today so they can collect favors tomorrow. That kind of self-interest is toxic and creates a lot of negative reciprocity cycles.

Reciprocity triggers the number one and number two of Kahle's LOV values of being well respected and warm relationships with others. Reciprocity builds trust according to Rilling & Sanfey, which increases the stability in a relationship.

Reciprocity affects workplace relationships, too. The balanced reciprocity of mutual interest boosts relationship quality according to Uhl-Bien & Maslyn. But people expect favors to be returned promptly and to be of equal value. Problems occur when that does not happen. In the workplace, while the follower receives salary, benefits, and hopefully psychological benefits, the leader gets something different. If the leader is good, the leader receives respect and loyalty which results in a boost to his or her status.

Looking at our narrative, in the beginning there was only basic workplace reciprocity in Jim and John's relationship. However, over time, the relationship started to grow, and possibilities for exchange occurred. This shows that a balanced exchange of favors will strengthen a relationship.

Status: Acknowledgement of Position and Prestige

Status is measured by how much an individual feels accepted by others, as well as his or her place or position in the group. Status is the element that makes us sensitive to hierarchy and our place in it and triggers the reward mechanism in the brain. It plays a strong role in a person's satisfaction with the relationship as it is related to respect and recognition, according to both Lieberman and Rilling & Sanfey. Historically, status was more important to men than it was to women, but in my research, gender did not make a difference.

Status is complex in that it encompasses four values of the LOV: sense of belonging, being well respected, sense of accomplishment, and self-fulfillment. By itself, by the absence of, or by being insufficient, status would not lead to a poor-quality relationship. But when combining it with the deterioration of one of the other elements, it can accelerate the deterioration of the leader-follower relationship.

Your place in the hierarchy is status. But what happens when the hierarchy is flattened? That is the norm these days as organizations remove levels of management.

There have always been many ways to show status. It could be your title, the corner office with a window, the furniture in that office, or the parking place. In some plants, the color of the hardhats indicates status. Those status markers were well known.

As organizational hierarchies flatten, it is more important for the leader to provide praise and recognition to followers so they feel valued. Status is not always clear cut and it varies from organization to organization. Status is still important, even if the markers and methods change.

Once again, in our narrative, what Jim and John had in common was lack of status. Neither felt valued by the company. Jeff and Sarah, with the help of Barry, reassured John that he was still important. First Jeff and Sarah reassured Jim that he was valued, and then John was able to reinforce that he also valued Jim.

Mutual Recognition Respect: Respect of Individual Rights and Humanity Through Recognition of Everyone's Worth and Dignity

Mutuality goes even further in supporting relationships with mutual recognition respect, which means valuing another person simply because he/she is a human being. It focuses on human worth as opposed to an assessment of capabilities. Mutual recognition respect comes close to unconditional acceptance. It precipitates the highest levels of self-esteem according to Clarke & Mahadi.

Neither Jim nor John respected the other person in the beginning. However, when they shifted their mindset, they realized that they were both an "us" and not a "them." After coming to that realization, they were able to recognize each other's humanity.

In summary, the seven *Implicit Social Elements*® are the building blocks of relationships. They are unconscious and implicit and play out in all leader-follower relationships.

CHAPTER FIVE: RECOMMENDATIONS FOR LEADERS AND FOLLOWERS

Leaders and Followers Shared Responsibility

Throughout my research, I have interviewed different people from a variety of roles and organizations and asked them 'what would happen if the relationship between leaders and followers improved?'. The answers were: we would be more productive, we would be happier, it would be more fun, and it would be less stressful.

It is important to understand who is responsible for the quality of a relationship between leaders and followers. Is it the leader? Many commentators would say, "Yes," and they would be right. But that is not the whole answer. It takes more than one person to make a relationship successful, and it is our responsibility to look at the leader and the follower as both having a role to play.

The best leader in the world cannot save a relationship by him/herself. If a follower is angry, resentful, and passive-aggressive, it may have nothing to do with the leader and, therefore, the leader is not the problem. Further evidence to support this would be if the same leader has great relationships with other followers.

Leaders and followers have separate tasks that positively or negatively affect relationship quality. The leader sets a tone for followers. If he or she acts like a transformative, servant, or emotionally intelligent leader, it is easier for followers to act authentically.

Followers have responsibilities too. Leaders have a right to expect the basics like loyalty, reliability, being a team player, and honesty. When it comes to relationships, good followership is as important as good leadership. Both need to work on the relationship taking into account the differences in their roles.

This may be difficult to realize in many organizations, as it involves more risk for the follower than the leader. We work in complex systems with a lot of moving parts. However, joint responsibility is true for all relationships.

Journey to Improving the Leader-Follower Relationship

The implicit leader and follower theories are interesting because they get to the heart of whether we believe that someone is worthy of our attention. The crazy part of this mental process is that it is unconscious and most people are unaware that they are doing it! This dynamic that occurs in the space between us. This energy exchange is what I wanted to explore, define and then measure. My challenge was in finding a tool that could measure these unconscious thoughts.

Well, I created such a tool! It's called the Leader-Follower Relationship Tool. This on-line survey measures the quality of the relationship between leaders and followers, and gives the relationship a score. *The Implicit Social Elements*® are related to the final score using statistical analysis. The tool has been validated, which means that it really does measure the relationship quality and *The Implicit Social Elements*®. For best results from the tool, the group size of a study needs to be 200 or more, so that the data can be statistically analyzed. If you want a study of a smaller number of people, then the results would be based on percentages. The tool can be utilized both ways. Please see Appendix 2 for a full description and the steps for how to improve the leader-follower relationship.

Below you will find recommendations on positively affecting each of *The Implicit Social Elements*®. The suggestions are simplistic, and in many cases, commonsensical. In an ideal world, these conversations would work easily. You can pull SMS (Situation Management Systems which is described in Appendix 2) in to conduct a survey or you can have the conversations yourself. You may need an expert in human development or organizational development to help you have these conversations. You can also look for ways to have the conversation while minimizing the risk.

Training in the influence skills would be tremendously helpful. For some of the implications and recommendations for enhancing *The Implicit Social Elements*®, the tasks for the leader or the follower are the same and thus there will only be one list for both. For the rest, you will find separate lists.

Items marked with an asterisk (*) are taught in the SMS' Positive Power and Influence Program®, mentioned in the appendices.

Let's start with trust.

Recommendations for Building Trust for Leaders:

Trust is an interesting element as it is affected by the other six elements. For example, if I feel respected by you, if you have self-control, if you are fair to me, if our relationship has reciprocity, if you empathize with me, if my status with you is clear – sometimes if any or all of these things exist - I trust you more. Trust is complicated, takes time to build, and can be destroyed in a nano-second. Here are some suggestions for building trust.

1. Be predictable. People should not have to figure out which personality they are dealing with today. (Self-Control)
2. Be genuine and authentic.
3. Admit when you make a mistake and apologize.
4. Deal directly and calmly with conflict and difficult situations.
5. Don't talk about people behind their backs. Don't get involved with gossip.
6. Define what fairness means. There are different ways that people judge if something is fair or not. Create policies that support the definition. (Fairness)
7. Give all direct reports your undivided attention regularly and actively listen to their issues. (Empathy)
8. Be as open as you can be, and communicate clearly when and why there is information that you cannot share.
9. Be clear about what you expect from your direct reports. Make sure they know the consequences of good and unacceptable performance and behavior. (Reciprocity)
10. Respect everyone just because they are human. Don't interrupt (apologize if you do). Tell the other person specifically what they are doing well. (Respect)
11. Recognize creativity even if it is off-target. Work with them to re-align. Recognize effort. Apologize when you blow it. (Respect)

12. Tell direct reports how much you value them. Let them know where they stand in the organization and what they can do to increase their standing. (Status)
13. Trust that direct reports will do the right thing. Accept that people are doing the best that they can, given their knowledge, skills, and abilities. Seek ways to improve trust that has been damaged.

Recommendations for Building Trust for Followers:

1. Be genuine and authentic.
2. Be as open as you can be, and explain why when you cannot be open.
3. Admit when you make a mistake and apologize.
4. Deal directly and calmly with conflict and difficult situations.
5. Don't talk about people behind their backs. Don't get involved with gossip.
6. Be predictable. People should not have to figure out which personality they are dealing with today. (Self-Control)
7. Understand that fairness is complicated. Have a frank and open discussion with your boss if you don't feel that you are being treated fairly. (Fairness)
8. Understand that your boss has a boss and sometimes he or she gets caught in the middle. Listen to your boss when they are feeling frustrated (Empathy)
9. Ask your boss for clarity about what he or she expects from you. Also, ask what the consequences are in case you will not be able to meet their expectations. Find out what you can do to help and support your boss. (Reciprocity)
10. Respect everyone just because they are human. Listen. Tell your boss what you like about working with him or her, and what your boss has done that impresses you. (Respect)
11. Explicitly ask your boss where you stand in the organization, and what you can do to increase your standing. Be prepared for challenging news and handle it with self-control. (Status)
12. Trust that your boss will try to do the right thing. If trust is damaged, look for ways to repair it. Trust your boss when they

communicate when and why there is information that they cannot share.

Recommendations for Creating Fairness for Leaders:

People define fairness in at least three different ways: everyone is treated the same, people are treated according to what they need, and people are treated in a way that recognizes what they have contributed. Most people don't think through fairness in this way but they do know when they feel like they have been treated either fairly or unfairly. It is a messy element, and most organizations are woefully inadequate when it comes to policies that deal with fairness. There is institutional fairness about how people are rewarded, jobs are assigned, and how information is shared. Here are some suggestions for building fairness.

1. Have a discussion with your direct reports to develop a common definition of fairness. Create operating practices that support this definition. Let the definition and practices evolve as you all learn how to create a "fair" work environment.

2. Implement and model the fairness guidelines you co-create with your group. Ask for feedback on how you are doing.

3. Every leader has some people he or she is more comfortable with. That is natural. It is easy to find yourself spending more time with those people and joking around with them. Stop doing that!

4. Spend your time with people based on what will make your team more effective. Joke around with everyone as it will prevent feelings of favoritism.

5. Be transparent about how job and salary decisions are made. People should understand the reasoning behind decisions that affect them.

6. Treat all direct reports in a kind, honest, and respectful way. If you must fire or lay off a person, treat them with dignity and respect.

Recommendations for Creating Fairness for Followers:

1. Suggest to your manager that the group discuss what it means to be treated fairly.
2. Participate openly in a discussion about fairness and state openly what it means to you.
3. If you feel that you have not been treated fairly, talk to your manager and explain why.
4. Be fair with your boss, and give him or her the benefit of the doubt.

Recommendations for Increasing Self-control for Leaders and Followers:

Self-control can include a range of behaviors that can span emotional self-control at the one end to dealing with different types of addiction on the other end. In the workplace we are mostly looking at issues concerning being behaviorally predictable, getting unpleasant tasks completed, and staying on schedule. Here are some suggestions for building self-control:

1. Be predictable. People who are mercurial are not trusted.
2. Create and follow schedules and deadlines. Deliver on your promises.
3. Don't be afraid to show what you are passionate about, but don't go over the top.
4. Handle conflict calmly. If a direct report/ leader is upset, use Listening* to help them calm down.
5. Develop the discipline to do hard and unpleasant tasks. Always be willing to have difficult conversations.

Manage your thoughts and emotions; do not get angry and yell at people, and control your thoughts so you don't get lost in the past or future. Learn emotion management techniques such as Disclosure*, Disengaging*, and reframing.

Recommendations for Building Empathy for Leaders and Followers:

Empathy is the ability to pay focused attention to another person. Listen* to what they are saying. Do not shift the focus of attention to yourself. Let them know through active listening that you understand what they are saying, thinking, and feeling. It's the good old advice of putting yourself in another's shoes. Understand that this is very difficult to do, our brain is designed to understand the world from our own perspective. Practice helps a lot! Here are some ways to be more empathic.

1. Be kind, genuine, and caring.
2. Only make suggestions when asked for ideas.
3. Anticipate the issues but don't push your understanding. Listen* intently.
4. Listen* for what the other person is feeling as well as what they are saying.
5. Notice when a direct report/leader is having difficulties and stop pushing your agenda. Take the time to listen* and understand the situation before making any suggestions.
6. Get grounded and manage your energy so that others feel that they can be open with you. Be balanced between your head, heart, and gut.
7. If you agree with what you hear, tell the other person what makes you feel the same way. Then, ask open-ended questions (Involving*) to encourage the other person to continue talking.
8. Value direct report's/leader's opinions, needs, ideas, and feelings. This is internal and has to do with how you think or feel about them. If you don't respect them, it will be difficult to listen to what they have to say.
9. Pay attention. Turn away from your computer, silence notifications on all devices, do not answer a landline. Then focus on the other person and on what they are saying. The other person should be doing most of the talking. If you are talking more, your attempt at empathy has failed.

10. If you have a negative reaction to what you hear, Disclose* what you are thinking without being judgmental or accusatory. One way to do this is to describe what you are thinking without using adjectives. This is not empathy, but it allows you to stay present. Suppressing your feelings tends to fail because we often leak what we are feeling.

Recommendations for Building Reciprocity for Leaders:

Some cultures require reciprocity. Everything is quid pro quo. We're often not explicit about the exchanges we make. We assume that others will give back after we have given to them in some way. Reciprocity is part of how we live in organizations. This is mostly explicit. You are hired, given a salary and benefits and there are expectations about your contribution in return. The leader benefits from having loyal followers and, therefore, having higher status. But what about the more informal types of reciprocity? Some people keep score consciously. Others are only vaguely aware of favors they owe and that others owe them. Here are some ideas about reciprocity.

1. Surprise everyone and bring in goodies to recognize a good week.
2. If a direct report does a really good job, recognize it in some way other than an email that says thanks.
3. If a direct report opens up, is vulnerable, and Discloses* something to you, find something appropriate to genuinely disclose back.
4. When a direct report does an outstanding job, be sure to praise them for it. You might consider a special reward such as a personal day off. Make sure the employee sees it as a reward.
5. Don't keep score, take the higher road. If you do something extra for someone, don't expect something in return. If someone gives back, be warm and appreciative. Thank them.
6. If a direct report wants a promotion, a raise, or another benefit, tell them clearly what the pathway is to get it according to corporate guidelines. If they do everything you ask, advocate for their raise/promotion without hesitation, by going through the organization's process.

Recommendations for Building Reciprocity for Followers:

1. Reciprocate gifts, coffee, donuts, lottery tickets, and smiles.
2. Say positive things about your boss to other people in the organization.
3. Give your boss the benefit of doubt. They believe in you, so you should believe in them.
4. If your boss stops and asks about your day/family/life, respond sincerely. It will help develop the relationship.
5. If you get a great project to work on, of course you'll do your best, but also be loyal to your boss. Support them every chance you get.
6. If your boss is trying to implement a new procedure, policy, or practice, encourage and help by being open, supportive, and creative.
7. Don't take gestures of generosity from your boss for granted. Do something nice in return. A handwritten thank-you note is powerful!

Recommendations for Increasing Status for Leaders:

How we think of status is changing. In the US, status used to be communicated with titles. Now connections and relationships are important, too. Many organizations are flat and don't have much of a hierarchy. People rely on relationships to understand how much they are valued. Here are some ideas about status:
1. Recognize direct reports for their achievements.
2. Laugh and joke around with everyone, not just the folks you like a lot.
3. Help others in the organization see the talent of your direct reports. Advocate for them.
4. Give your direct reports frequent and usable feedback so they know how they're doing and how they could improve.
5. Reward direct reports who go above and beyond. Make sure everyone has opportunities to go above and beyond.

6. Tell direct reports how much you value them. Do it a lot. If they are weaker performers, help them get better, coach and mentor them.

7. Let all your direct reports know where they stand in terms of their career. Help them advance, work with them, find them mentors. Maybe you need to help them find a better fit.

8. Give everyone a chance at exciting projects that will develop them. Work on giving everyone work that is exciting for them. Sometimes, you may need to explain that it is just getting the normal tasks completed versus always being involved in an exciting project – both build reputation and status.

Recommendations for Increasing Status for Followers:

1. If you don't know where you stand in terms of your career, ask your manager. Be prepared and be strong - sometimes feedback can be hard to hear.

2. Believe in yourself!

3. Listen to and accept feedback.

4. Act on the feedback and better yourself.

5. Do things for the greater good, be generous with your time.

6. Being valued is more than an intellectual exercise. Contribute to the emotional wellbeing of others as well.

Recommendations for Building Mutual Recognition Respect for Leaders and Followers:

Mutual recognition respect is simply respecting everyone because they are a human being. There are many ways to show respect, but here are a few ideas:

1. You don't have to win.

2. Build Common Ground*.

3. Don't call people names.

4. Accept everyone unconditionally.
5. Listen* carefully to what others have to say.
6. Don't talk about people behind their backs.
7. Do not talk over, interrupt, or argue with anyone.
8. If someone is excited about something, help them express it.
9. Accept that everyone is doing the best that they can, given who they are.
10. Always apologize when you blow it, even if you don't think you did, but someone else does.
11. Wash the dishes and take out the trash. Seriously, every workplace has housekeeping chores. Do your share!

These are some suggestions about how to look at your relationships from the perspective of *The Implicit Social Elements*®. I have developed a tool (which is described in Appendix 2) that can measure the quality of the relationships in your organization between leaders and followers. You can use it to help understand and improve your company culture. Thriving leader-follower relationships are the hallmark of a healthy and productive company culture. In the next chapter we will review how to create thriving relationships.

CHAPTER SIX: CREATING THRIVING RELATIONSHIPS

Relationships can be beautiful. They can also be painful. They can teach you about yourself. They can help you blame others for who you are instead of owning your own stuff. Relationships are a painful requirement and a beautiful walk on a summer's evening. They can support you in hard times, or they can break your heart.

What else can raise us to an ecstatic level of jubilation and seconds later pitch us down into the depths of despair? Pretty much everything we do and the decisions we make are based on relationships.

In a new start-up, founders work together to create a structure around a product or service. They agree on some things and disagree on others. The ways they deal with conflict lay the groundwork for the company culture. Eventually an organization (org) chart shows who reports to whom, but the chart is never the whole story.

A web of other relationships exists that never appears on the org chart. People get things done through their relationships, not the org chart. Melanie helped people who worked for Mr. Corbin stay safe and get things done. Sarah and Jeff helped Jim understand his boss. And Barry used his long-standing relationship with Mr. Corbin to help him change.

I have been telling clients for years that influence lives in the space between us. Each one of us in the room contributes to the outcome and the quality of the relationship. The deep curiosity that drove my PhD study was to understand all of the obvious and not so obvious factors that affect relationships. I wanted to know how they work and how we can improve them.

Since then, I have learned a lot. I used interdisciplinary methods to study the way humans act in social situations. I identified seven *Implicit Social Elements*® that people use in social relationships. I concentrated my research on the impact of those elements on leader-follower relationships.

I wanted to give you a sense of the hard science behind *The Implicit Social Elements®* without making that science difficult. I put the science first in the book because I believe it is important to understand the science to apply the principles effectively. I have told you about the implication of the science, and illustrated them with the story of Jim and John. But, if all you do is read the book and improve your understanding, I will have failed.

I did not write this book because I needed another big project on my to-do list. I wrote it with the hope that, after reading the book, you would behave differently than before you picked it up. Here's how I hope your life will be different from now on.

Understand How Systems Affect Your Relationships

Systems are everywhere and impact everything. If something is not working, drawing boundaries around the issue and looking from a system's perspective can provide us with a unique vantage point. Whatever relationship you enter into, you are entering into a system whether it is a family, community or a work system. Whenever you do that, you give up a piece of yourself to fit in and make it work.

We create systems - biological, psychological, and social - as a way of creating understanding and meaning. At first, there is pure potential. We can always affect the way things work out. There's always pure potential to create whatever you want in every part of your life.

What comes next is pure experience. Most of this is unconscious. When Jim stood in front of Mr. Corbin's desk during his "torture session," he experienced many things. There were the sensations of being in the room, of hearing Mr. Corbin carrying on. There were memories of previous encounters with Mr. Corbin and others. This lasts for an instant before we move on to the next level.

The next level is pure synthesis. We start making sense of experience. Jim might have remembered being in the principal's office in elementary school. He might have replayed encounters with other leaders. When you have made sense of the experience, you can move on to the next level. I call that one "pure intention." At this point, you make judgements and choices. When you act on those choices, that is "pure lived reality."

Every situation is different. But you can always influence the way things work out. This is simply a system of knowledge, a place to begin understanding. Every organization has a multitude of systems that organize the business and manage tasks and people. There are inputs and outputs and unpredictable elements in every system.

Start looking from a system's perspective to have a more objective view. Consider theories like panarchy that look at complex adaptive systems. Panarchy evolved based on the observations and adaptability of ecosystems. If you look up panarchy you will find that the original word was coined in the 1800's, but I am referring to the work of Gunderson and Holling.

Understanding systems adds an interesting dimension as you look at your effectiveness in your relationships. What is the impact you are having as an input into the family, community, or work systems you are involved in?

Be More Conscious of How Our Brains Work to Affect Our Relationships

Over eons, we have evolved a brain that does most of its work unconsciously. If that weren't so, we would be overwhelmed by the number of decisions and observations we must make every second of every day. Our brains make it easy for us by doing most of the work outside of our awareness.

That is great most of the time. But sometimes, you need to break into the unconscious process and make a conscious decision. To do that, you should understand how our brains work in any social situation.

The Default Mode Network plays a central role in how we connect with others. Much of that work is unconscious and we are unaware of how important the *Implicit Social Elements*® are in every relationship. Start making choices about how you react and respond in situations where the relationships are not as good as you would like them to be.

Do you have unconscious needs to be a winner, to be in control, or to be right? It's impossible to have quality relationships if you have needs such as these. Examine yourself first!

Relationships Are Part of What Makes Great Work Teams Great

If you are a business leader, you know that it is important to "make your numbers." You and your team are responsible for certain results. Many business leaders think that's all there is. They're sure that, if they achieve their goals and make their numbers, everything will be great. But that is not true.

Great companies and great leaders know that the relationships are as important as making the numbers. Strong relationships among team members make teams more productive. Sure, you can achieve your goals without paying attention to relationships, but then you only have the potential for short-term success. Teams with strong relationships can create great results today and set you up for great results tomorrow.

Research from MIT indicates that the most productive teams provide strong social support for team members. As a leader, you can use your understanding of relationships to create a team that gets great results and also establish a great place to work.

Reflect on Your Relationships

Think constantly about how you can improve your relationships. If you are not getting the things done that need to get done or you are frustrated much of the time, reflect on your relationships. If you feel like no one's listening to you, reflect on your relationships. If your projects are not coming out the way you want them, reflect on your relationships.

If things are not going well, you can ask the following questions:

1. What am I doing?
2. What should I do differently?
3. How can I create a different and better outcome with the people on my team?
4. What am I contributing to the mess?

When you want things to be different, start by analyzing your behavior. Decide what you should do differently.

There's Potential to Create Whatever Kind of Interaction You Want with Another Person

It does not matter how bad a relationship is. It does not matter how long the relationship has been bad. It does not matter if the other person does not seem to care. You have the potential to create whatever kind of interaction you want between yourself and the other person. An option is to simply say, I am sorry, please forgive me, and I care about our relationship. Now see the impact saying that has on the relationship!

You cannot "make" anyone else do anything or feel anything. But you can make choices from your side and contribute from your side to the quality of the relationship and the quality of the conversation.

If you rely on the brain's unconscious processes, it is not likely you can bring about the kind of change you want. You will be more effective managing relationships if you make conscious choices.

You can decide. Decide how you want the relationship to improve. Decide what you will do to help make that happen.

Analyze Relationships with *The Implicit Social Elements*®

- *The Implicit Social Elements*® give you a practical way to analyze any relationship so you can choose actions to improve it. Whether you are the leader or the follower in a relationship, you have the obligation to improve things.

- **Analyze trust.** Trust is your confidence in the honesty or integrity of another person. Look for opportunities to be more trustworthy.

- **Analyze fairness.** Fairness is the objective treatment of another person. People will judge your fairness in two ways. They will judge whether you treat them the same way you treat others who act the same way and they will evaluate your decision process.

- **Analyze your self-control.** Self-control is your ability to control your emotions in difficult and trying situations. It includes your ability to step up and do hard or unenjoyable tasks. Some of those tasks can be daunting, like talking to a team member about their performance or behavior. Self-control also includes your discipline to tackle difficult but important things.

- **Analyze your empathy.** Empathy is how well you recognize, understand, and share the feelings of others. It's your ability to "walk a mile in another person's shoes."

- **Analyze reciprocity.** Reciprocity is a core human value and appears in almost all cultures. When we do a favor for another person, it is generally expected that the favor will be returned at some point. But don't do an overabundance of favors for people because they will think that you are trying to build up a debt so you can ask for a big favor yourself.

- **Analyze status.** Status involves recognition and being valued. Praise people for good work. Thank them for their effort. Ask about things that matter to them.

- **Analyze mutual recognition and respect.** Mutual recognition respect represents our desire to be treated as individual, valuable human beings. Find ways to show that you value another person just for who they are.

If either Jim or John had analyzed the above elements at any point, they might not have needed outsiders to help them change. *The Implicit Social Elements®* give you a straightforward way to analyze any relationship.

You don't have to be at the mercy of unconscious mental processes. You have the understanding to improve the relationships that define your life and your leadership/followership. Use the Implicit Social Elements® to analyze situations and relationships. Then you can make wise conscious choices and act to make things better. Remember, there is always potential, get very clear on your intention, and go heal as many relationships as you can.

APPENDIX 1:
THE POSITIVE POWER AND INFLUENCE PROGRAM

Participants who attend the *POSITIVE POWER AND INFLUENCE*® Program have a deep desire to become more influential. They realize that they can achieve this goal through increased self-awareness, emotional intelligence, and the SMS influence tool kit.

The Challenge

Habitual reactions and behaviors block one's ability to calmly and creatively work with difficult people. The *POSITIVE POWER AND INFLUENCE*® Program teaches participants how to strategically change the way they interact with others, especially in difficult situations. Defensiveness, frustration, and apathy are replaced with strength and purpose through the use of the Influence Styles, which are essential to achieving objectives while building important relationships. Participants learn to diagnose difficult influence situations that they encounter, then construct a strategic Influence Action Plan. Many research studies have demonstrated the power of planning. In SMS' own research, we found that four weeks after attending the Program, 75% of participants have had success or have on-going success in challenging situations. Prior to attending the Program, only 25% felt they had a chance of succeeding.

The Purpose

Influence is an essential life skill and people do not separate their personal life from their professional life from a behavioral standpoint. Whether communicating with people in their workplace, community, or home, excellent influencers are keenly aware of the need to build trust, establish connections, be authentic, emotionally intelligent, and above all, be present. Influence occupies the space between people and any one person has the ability to shift the dynamics in the room. Getting things done with and through others includes meeting the needs of all parties involved, while simultaneously satisfying multiple agendas.

Yet, there needs to be a balance between achieving objectives and taking care of relationships. Based on neuroscience research, this can be extremely challenging given the way our brains are wired. We have two different neural networks directly involved with influencing; one that focuses on the task, which is called the task positive network, and one that focuses on relationships, which is called the default mode network. These networks often do not operate simultaneously, potentially resulting in the loss of productivity and effectiveness. People who favor the task positive network may achieve their influence objectives, but often at the expense of important relationships. Others, who favor the default mode network, habitually avoid conflict thereby preserving the relationship, but sometimes at the expense of fulfilling their work goals. Based on the neuroplasticity of the brain, this can be changed through the use of the Situational Influence Model™, mentioned in Appendix 2, which stimulates these two neural networks to get the task done and manage relationships at the same time.

By attending the *POSITIVE POWER AND INFLUENCE*® Program, participants learn about their strengths and weaknesses. It challenges them to take responsibility for the quality of their work and relationships versus blaming others – the difficult people, or the situation – for their inability to succeed. By applying the key elements of the Situational Influence Model, participants grasp how to influence others effectively, through managing their emotions and handling conflict.

Where INFLUENCE Matters...

• Manage emotions in difficult situations and with challenging people
• Increase self-awareness of impact on others
• Conduct more influential conversations that get results
• Influence others without the use of positional authority

- Build and maintain relationships at work, in the community, and at home
- Become more effective team members/team leaders

Who is the Target Audience?

- Leaders who need to influence change and build a foundation of trust and commitment
- Program or project managers who must obtain the cooperation of functional managers over whom they have no authority
- Salespeople who need to build trust-based consultative relationships with clients and prospects
- Technical or professional personnel who take on supervisory or management responsibilities
- Individuals who must exert influence cross-functionally
- Staff who need to gain the support of operating managers
- Managers and supervisors who want to develop their influence skills to lead more effectively
- Anyone whose responsibilities exceed his or her positional authority

What is in the Program?

The core of the *POSITIVE POWER AND INFLUENCE®* Program is the renowned Situational Influence Model™, which consists of three key elements: Influence Energy, Influence Styles, and Influence Behaviors. The Model demonstrates that we need not rely on one predominant Influence Style. Rather, we can apply the Styles best suited to each influence situation we encounter. We define Energy as mental, emotional, physical, and spiritual. When we feel strong in each of these areas, we convey that strength through being authentic, centered, and grounded. This type of energy immediately builds trust, and is expressed through our words, tone of voice, and body language. It is further defined as being Push, Pull, or Moving Away Energy.

Push

The influencer asserts his/her position or seeks to persuade key stakeholders.

Pull

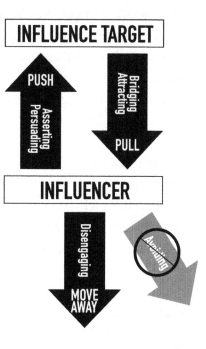

The influencer uses empathy or involving and cooperative behaviors to attract and build bridges to key stakeholders.

Move Away

The influencer, perceiving a deadlock or an insurmountable impasse, disengages and re-evaluates his/her influence strategy. Note: Disengaging is not avoiding, as the influencer is still actively seeking to influence key stakeholders.

How is the Program Structured?

The *POSITIVE POWER AND INFLUENCE*® Program moves briskly through influence concepts to focus participants on mastering Influence Behaviors, and to applying those Behaviors in their own work environment in the weeks immediately following the Program. This is accomplished through role-plays, case studies, small and large group work, exercises, lecturettes, one-on-one trainer coaching, peer feedback, a/v feedback, and application to a real-life situation. A key learning point for most people is that they need to manage their impact on others. Influence is not a one-way street and it is not something that we do to others. Based on our knowledge of a situation and the other person, if we communicate something that resonates with them then they will most likely respond positively. Without this resonance, influence does not occur.

SELF-ASSESSMENT: Prior to the Program, participants complete self-assessments on a productive and a less productive relationship, collecting data from associates via an online 360-degree feedback instrument. This data is used in conjunction with recorded exercises and in-program feedback to clearly identify which Influence Styles each participant tends to use, as well as to highlight their personal opportunities to become more influential.

DEVELOPING STYLE AND FLEXIBILITY: Participants learn the fundamentals of the Influence Styles they use infrequently or ineffectively. They also practice the Influence Styles with which they are already familiar, learning how to apply them more effectively. Participants thoroughly explore all Styles and develop personal learning goals for the remainder of the Program.

DEVELOPING INFLUENCE SKILLS: Participants engage in exercises using various Influence Styles in relevant and challenging situations to improve their ability to first diagnose the influence situation, craft an influence strategy using a diagnostic tool, then strategically sequence and apply the most effective Styles.

APPLICATION PLANNING: Lastly and most importantly, using a real situation and incorporating intensive feedback from peers and training staff, participants plan and rehearse that real-life influence situation.

How is the Program Delivered?

The *POSITIVE POWER AND INFLUENCE*® Program can be conducted in a variety of formats using SMS certified trainers:

- Face-to-face (1-, 2-, or 3-day programs) – In-house and public programs
- Virtual – All sessions are conducted online using break-out rooms for practice exercises
- Blended – A combination of face-to-face and virtual components

Your SMS account manager will work closely with you to customize the Program for your audience.

Note: We also encourage client organizations to conduct the Program using internal facilitators trained and certified by our firm.

Who Uses or has used the *POSITIVE POWER AND INFLUENCE®* Program?

More than a quarter million managers and professionals, working in the world's leading organizations, including:

- Alstom
- Arch Insurance
- Blue Cross Blue Shield
- Boston Scientific
- Colgate-Palmolive
- CVS
- Fannie Mae
- First Interstate Bank
- General Electric
- ISO New England
- Metro AG
- NASA
- NIH
- Procter & Gamble
- Salesforce
- Treasury Executive Institute
- US FDA
- Williams-Sonoma, Inc.
- World Bank Group

APPENDIX 2:
SITUATION MANAGEMENT SYSTEMS

Situation Management Systems, Inc. (SMS) was founded in 1976 as an applied behavioral science firm. We are a global training company that mentors organizations that want to invest in their people to develop their human potential. We provide relevant and applicable training solutions that address critical problems faced by forward-thinking organizations.

A certified small women-owned company, SMS is the original developer of the Positive Power and Influence® Program (smsinc.com). SMS specializes in the area of influence, and we know that individuals are most effective at influencing others when they are perceived as being authentic, trustworthy, respectful, and present. We not only teach influence as a core skill, but also demonstrate how it supports the implementation of other processes and strategies from a behavioral standpoint.

For over 40 years we have mentored people worldwide how to positively influence others. Our training programs include behavioral coaching to enhance emotional intelligence and organizational efficiency. Furthermore, our current research into neuroscience and quantum physics indicates a deeper need for social leadership. In actuality, we all flourish when this type of human development is an organizational priority. Imagine the culture that emerges from intentional social leadership!

SMS training programs are situation-based, allowing participants to learn new skills in the context of real-life situations. Experiential learning is very powerful and, therefore, our programs include individual practice and reflection, small group work, peer-to-peer and trainer feedback and coaching, and recorded exercises. Participants develop action plans for effectively applying new skills to the situations they encounter. Our training programs offer applicable real-life solutions to challenging real-life situations, and prepare participants to get work done in the real world, where individuals need to be flexible, adaptable, and focused on success.

We offer virtual programs (since 2012), as well as blended and face-to-face formats. SMS programs are currently offered in more than 50 countries and 15 languages.

Our Programs include:

- POSITIVE POWER AND INFLUENCE® Program
- Positive Negotiation Program
- Negotiation Strategy and Tactics
- Influencing Positive Change
- The Art and Neuroscience of Selling
- Creating Results
- Leading People for Successful Projects
- Leading Through Adversity

Our clients include Fortune 50 companies, mid-size corporations, non-profit organizations, and government agencies. Since the power to positively influence others is increasingly essential to individual and organizational success, everyone needs to be able to influence effectively regardless of industry or position.

SMS and our global network of partners are passionate about and committed to each and every individual and group with whom we work. Whether we are delivering an off-the-shelf program to executive assistants or a highly-customized program to a senior-level group, the result is the same... participants acquire skills that are relevant, effective, and immediately applicable. Our many years of experience in the industry have earned us the reputation of being a trustworthy partner to all of our clients, and we are dedicated to providing sustainable communication and leadership training for our clients.

Leader-Follower Relationship Consulting

SMS will mentor organizations to initiate the leader-follower journey and to successfully take each step and deliver the results. As a way to start your journey, initiate a change project to improve your organization's culture. Sometimes it is wise to choose a small part of the organization where people are open to growth and change, or you may decide to involve the whole organization. Let people know that you want to analyze the leader-follower relationship, and determine, using at least 200 people, who would fill out the survey as leaders and who as followers (as many are both). Then use The Leader-Follower Relationship Tool to collect data. Once everyone has completed the survey, you analyze the results.

After the analysis and interpretation comes the prioritization. What does your organization wish to keep or improve and where does it want to focus its resources? These steps should be done by both leaders and followers for greater impact and engagement through investing the time to brainstorm with people deep within the organization. As a compromise, take a sample of leaders and followers from different parts of the organization and empower them to make recommendations.

Once you have a set of priorities, you need to think about how you want to measure the results both for the things you wish to keep as well as the things that you wish to improve. These measures should be baselined, measured through and after the change project. Once comfortable, you need to set initial targets for the measures that are aligned to your change goals.

For example, the organization may find that Reciprocity, Self-Control and Mutual Recognition Respect correlate with a D-relationship score. From this and further research, the organization may conclude that leaders and followers should focus on understanding the exchange process between leaders and followers to discover changes that would positively impact the relationship around reciprocity. Mutual recognition respect is respecting others simply because they are human, therefore what are some ground rules around interactions to increase mutual respect? And finally, what steps do both leaders and followers need to take to improve their self-control when it comes to emotion management and impulse control?

With the prioritization and measures in your pocket, you then develop the strategy and plan to achieve the change goals. As you get into the details of the strategy and plan you will develop further prioritizing, timing, and more detailed targets. Again, it is really important to think about engaging the greater organization in the plan. The leaders and followers will really appreciate the energy and intent, and will energize themselves to help.

As part of the plan definition, choose a time or times to repeat the Leader-Follower Relationship Survey to either monitor progress or check results of all the efforts. For progress monitoring samples of the organization can be used, but I recommend doing a full organizational survey as a post change project check to obtain a truest measure of the results. Then comes the implementation.

To summarize, the following seven steps are recommended toward your journey to improving your organization's leader-follower relationship:

1. Initiate a change project that addresses organizational culture including looking at the leader-follower relationship;
2. Perform a study using the on-line Leader-Follower Relationship Tool;
3. Analyze and interpret the results from the survey/tool through engagement;
4. Prioritize *The Implicit Social Elements*® and decide which of them the organization wishes to improve;
5. Define a strategy for improvement, engage the whole or a small part of the organization, and install measures;
6. Implement and track progress;
7. Perform post-Study using Leader-Follower Relationship Tool.

From my experience, most of the change required in improving the leader-follower relationship is helping leaders and followers develop their skills and confidence in being adaptable in their approaches to different circumstances and people situations. With this, the relationships will improve. Arming people with such skills and confidence brings us back to *Positive Power and Influence*® (PPI). PPI has been proven as the best program for this human development, and an organization's change strategy and plan often includes the roll out of a comprehensive PPI training program focused on the areas of priority.

In your journey to improve your organization's culture SMS can mentor you in the following ways:

1. Consulting on culture change, change management, the leader-follower relationship, and *The Implicit Social Elements*® and tools
2. Provide the Leader-Follower Relationship on-line survey and documentation
3. Consult on the analysis and interpretation of the survey results
4. Facilitate brainstorming, engagement, and prioritization
5. Consult on strategy and planning
6. Provide *Positive Power and Influence*® programs - customized or standard
7. Provide custom training plans and programs to meet specific change needs
8. Perform sample and full organizational leader surveys.

REFERENCES

Alves, P.N., Foulon, C., Karolis, V. *et al.* An improved neuroanatomical model of the default-mode network reconciles previous neuroimaging and neuropathological findings. *Commun Biol* **2**, 370 (2019). https://doi.org/10.1038/s42003-019-0611-3

Bechara, A. (2005). Decision making, impulse control and loss of willpower to resist drugs: a neurocognitive perspective. *Nature Neuroscience*, 8(11), 1458-63.

Berscheid, E. (1994). Interpersonal relationships. *Annual Review of Psychology*, 45, 79-129.

Bohm, D. (1989). *An interview with David Bohm*. Retrieved from https://www.youtube.com/watch?v=SvyD2o7w24g

Bohm, D. (1994). *Thought as a system*. New York, NY: Taylor & Francis.

Bohm, D. (2005). *Wholeness and the implicate order*. New York, NY: Taylor & Francis.

Boyatzis, R. (2011). Managerial and leadership competencies: A behavioral approach to emotional, social and cognitive intelligence. *Vision*, 15(2), 91-100.

Boyatzis, R., Goleman, D., McKee, A. (2013). *Primal leadership*. Boston, MA: Harvard Business School.

Boyatzis, R., Rochford, K., & Jack, A. (2014). Antagonistic neural networks underlying differentiated leadership roles. *Frontiers in Human Neuroscicence*. http://dx.doi.org/10.3389/fnhum.2014.00114

Brier, S. (2008). *Cybersemiotics: Why information is not enough.* Toronto, Canada: University of Toronto Press.

Brier, S. (2013a). Cybersemiotics: A new foundation for transdisciplinary theory of information, cognition, meaningful communication and the interaction between nature and culture. *Integral Review,* 9(2), 220-263.

Brier, S. (2013b). Professor Brier presents cyber[bio]semiotics, through Bateson, Luhmann, and Pierce. Retrieved from: https://www.youtube.com/watch?v=f_AOiJWu7rE

Brier, S. (2014). The riddle of the Sphinx answered: On how C.S. Peirce's transdisciplinary semiotic philosophy links science and spirituality. In C. Tandy (Ed.), *Death and anti-death, Volume 12: One hundred years after Charles S. Peirce (1839-1914).* Ann Arbor, MI: Ria University Press.

Brier, S. (2015). Finding an information concept suited for a universal theory of information. *Progress in Biophysics and Molecular Biology.* Retrieved from https://www.researchgate.net/publication/279635518_For_Progress_in_Biophysics_and_Molecular_biology_Special_theme_issue_on_Integral_Biomathics_Life_Sciences_Mathematics_and_Phenomenological_Philosophy

Brier, S. (2017). Peircean cosmogony's symbolic agapistic self-organization as an example of the influence of eastern philosophy on western thinking. *Progress in Biophysics and Molecular Biology,* 131, 92-107.

Burger, J. M., Sanchez, J., Imberi, J. E., Grande, L. R. (2009). The norm of reciprocity as an internalized social norm: Returning favors even when no one finds out. *Psychology Press,* 4(1), 11-17.

Cialdini, R. (1994). *Influence: The psychology of persuasion*, New York, NY: HarperCollins

Clarke, N., & Mahadi, N. (2017). Mutual recognition respect between leaders and follower: Its relationship to follower job performance and well-being. *Journal of Business Ethics*, 141(1), 163-178.

Foxall, G. (2014). Cognitive requirements of competing neuro-behavioral decision systems: some implications of temporal horizon for managerial behavior in organizations. *Frontiers in Human Neuroscience*. http://dx.doi.org/10.3389/fnhum.2014.00184

Gunderson, L., & Holling, C. S. (Eds.) (2002). *Panarchy: Understanding transformations in human and natural systems.* Washington, DC: Island Press.

Holmes, J. G. (1991). Trust and the appraisal process in close relationships. In W. H. Jones & D. Perlman (Eds.), *Advances in personal relationships: A research annual,* 2, 57-104: Oxford, England: Jessica Kingsley Publishers.

Kahle, L. R. (Ed). (1983). *Social values and social change.* New York, NY: Praeger.

Kahle, L. R., Kennedy, P. (1988). Using the list of values (LOV) to understand consumers. *The Journal of Services Marketing,* 2, 49-56.

Lieberman, M. D. (2000). Intuition: A social cognitive neuroscience approach. *Psychological Bulletin*, 126(1), 109-137.

Lieberman, M. D. (2007). Social cognitive neuroscience: A review of core processes. *Annual Review of Psychology,* 58(1), 259–289.

Lieberman, M. D. (2013). *Social: why our brains are wired to connect.* New York, NY: Crown Random House.

Malouf, S. (2019). *The Impact of the Implicit Social Elements® on the Quality of the Leader-Follower Relationship.* https://search.proquest.com/openview/1e5e9f53775a84305efe2129d4d0c85d/1?pq-origsite=gscholar&cbl=18750&diss=y

Meadows, D. (2004). *Thinking in systems.* White River Junction, VT: Sustainability Institute.

Peirce, C. S. (1940). *The philosophy of Peirce: Selected writings.* New York, NY: Dover Publications.

Rilling, J. K., & Sanfey, A. G. (2011). The Neuroscience of Social Decision-Making. *Annual Review of Psychology, 62,* 23-48. doi: 10.1146/annurev.psych.121208.131647

Salazar, L. R. (2015). The negative reciprocity process in marital relationships: A literature review. *Aggression and Violent Behavior, 24,* 113-119.

Sapolsky, R. M. (2017). *Behave: The biology of humans at our best and worst.* New York, NY: Penguin Press.

Siegel, D. J. (2001). Toward an interpersonal neurobiology of the developing mind: attachment relationships, "mindsight," and neural integration. *Infant Mental Health Journal, 22*(1-2), 67–94.

Siegel, D. J. (2012). *A pocket guide to interpersonal neurobiology: an integrative handbook of the mind.* New York, NY: W. W. Norton.

Whatley, M. A., Webster, M., Smith, R. H., & Rhodes, A. (2010). The effect of a favor on public and private compliance: how internalized is the norm of reciprocity? *Basic and Applied Social*

Psychology, 21(3), 251-259.

Zak, P. J., Kurzban, R., & Matzner, W. (2004). The neurobiology of trust. *Annals of the New York Academy of Science*, 1032(1).

Made in the USA
Middletown, DE
20 March 2021